Student Lecture Notebook and Study Companion

Martini

Fundamentals of Anatomy and Physiology, 5/e

LEARNING
SYSTEM
Edition

D1530427

Contents

To the Student

This Student Lecture Notebook and Study Companion is designed to be a valuable resource that will help you do your best in this anatomy and physiology course.

- Each chapter begins with a Chapter Outline and Chapter Objectives from the text. If your study focuses on this outline and understanding and being able to answer the chapter objectives, you will most likely be prepared for the course tests. Additional help—including self-grading quizzes—is available on the web site that accompanies your text.
- Key illustrations from the textbook and the Instructor's Transparency Set are reproduced in this notebook. Because you won't have to redraw the art in class, you can focus your attention on the instructor's lecture and take your notes in this book. Leave all of your notes together or remove them and organize them by chapter with your SYSTEM EDITION text.

CHAPTER

1   An Introduction to Anatomy and Physiology

CHAPTER OUTLINE

INTRODUCTION
THE SCIENCES OF ANATOMY AND PHYSIOLOGY
ANATOMY
PHYSIOLOGY
LEVELS OF ORGANIZATION
HOMEOSTASIS AND SYSTEM INTEGRATION
NEGATIVE FEEDBACK
POSITIVE FEEDBACK
A FRAME OF REFERENCE FOR ANATOMICAL STUDIES
SUPERFICIAL ANATOMY
SECTIONAL ANATOMY

CHAPTER OBJECTIVES

1. Describe the basic functions of organisms.
2. Define anatomy and physiology, and describe various specialties of each discipline.
3. Identify the major levels of organization in organisms, from the simplest to the most complex.
4. Identify the organ systems of the human body and the major components of each system.
5. Explain the concept of homeostasis and its significance for organisms.
6. Describe how positive feedback and negative feedback are involved in homeostatic regulation.
7. Use anatomical terms to describe body sections, body regions, and relative positions.
8. Identify the major body cavities and their subdivisions.

•FIGURE 1-1 Levels of Organization

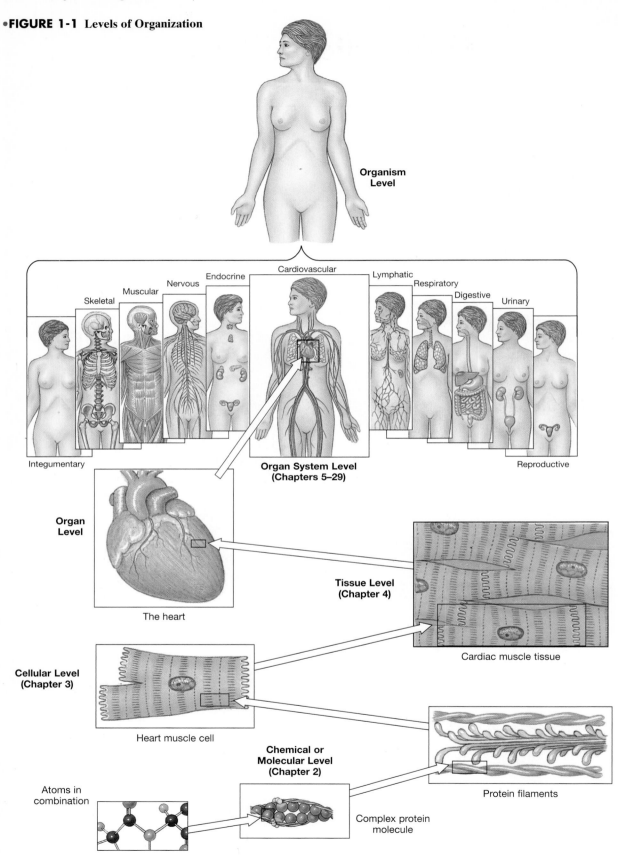

Organism
Level

Skeletal

Muscular

Nervous

Endocrine

Cardiovascular

Lymphatic

Respiratory

Digestive

Urinary

Integumentary

Organ System Level
(Chapters 5–29)

Reproductive

Organ
Level

The heart

Tissue Level
(Chapter 4)

Cardiac muscle tissue

Cellular Level
(Chapter 3)

Heart muscle cell

Chemical or
Molecular Level
(Chapter 2)

Atoms in
combination

Complex protein
molecule

Protein filaments

© 2002 Prentice Hall, Inc.

NOTES

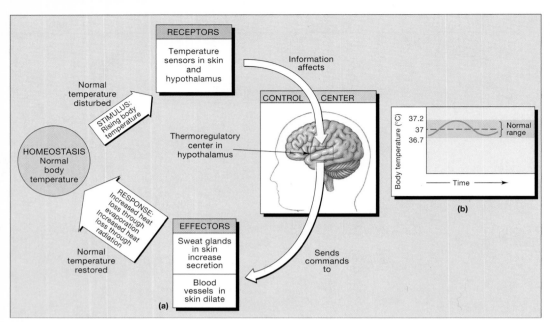

•FIGURE 1-4
Negative
Feedback:
The Control
of Body
Temperature

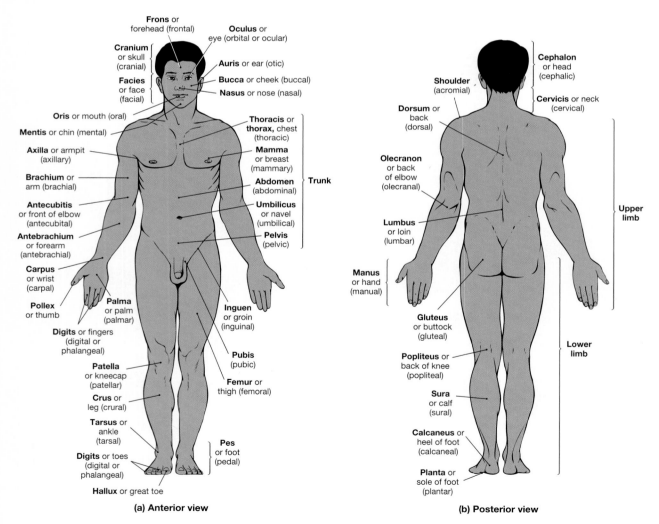

(a) Anterior view

(b) Posterior view

•FIGURE 1-6 Anatomical Landmarks

NOTES

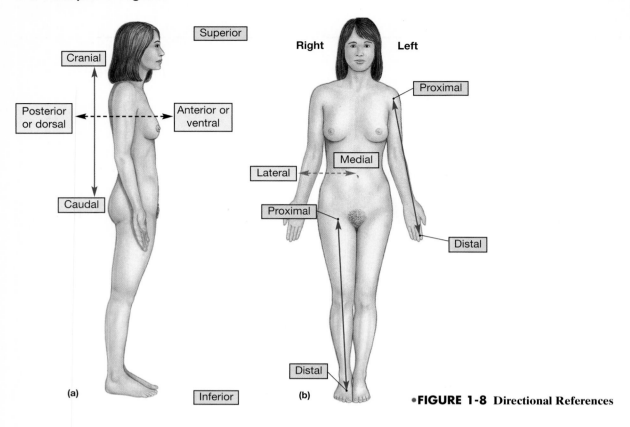

(a)

(b)

•FIGURE 1-8 Directional References

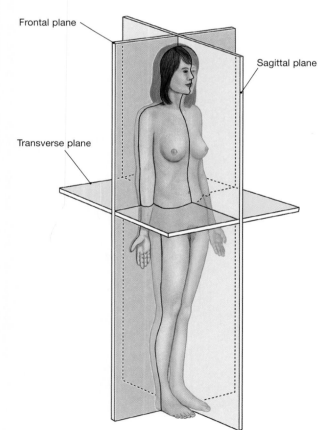

•FIGURE 1-9 Planes of Section

NOTES

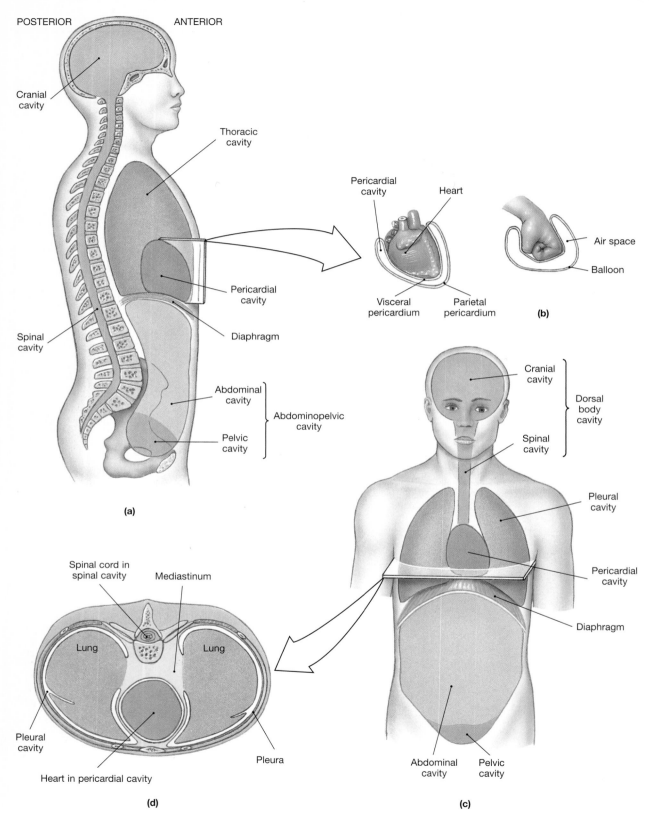

POSTERIOR   ANTERIOR

Cranial
cavity

Thoracic
cavity

Pericardial
cavity   Heart

Air space

Balloon

Visceral   Parietal
pericardium   pericardium   (b)

Spinal
cavity

Pericardial
cavity

Diaphragm

Abdominal
cavity

Abdominopelvic
cavity

Pelvic
cavity

(a)

Cranial
cavity

Dorsal
body
cavity

Spinal
cavity

Pleural
cavity

Pericardial
cavity

Diaphragm

Abdominal   Pelvic
cavity   cavity

(c)

Spinal cord in
spinal cavity   Mediastinum

Lung   Lung

Pleural
cavity

Pleura

Heart in pericardial cavity

(d)

•FIGURE 1-11 Body Cavities

NOTES

CHAPTER

2   The Chemical Level of Organization

CHAPTER OUTLINE

CHAPTER OBJECTIVES

1. Describe an atom and how atomic structure affects interactions between atoms.
2. Compare the ways in which atoms combine to form molecules and compounds.
3. Use chemical notation to symbolize chemical reactions.
4. Distinguish among the major types of chemical reactions that are important for studying physiology.
5. Describe the crucial role of enzymes in metabolism.
6. Distinguish between organic and inorganic compounds.
7. Explain how the chemical properties of water make life possible.
8. Discuss the importance of pH and the role of buffers in body fluids.
9. Describe the physiological roles of inorganic compounds.
10. Discuss the structures and functions of carbohydrates, lipids, proteins, nucleic acids, and high-energy compounds.

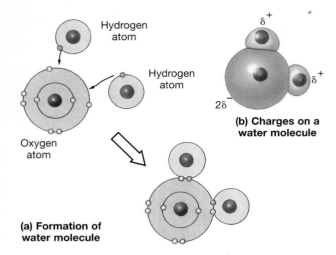

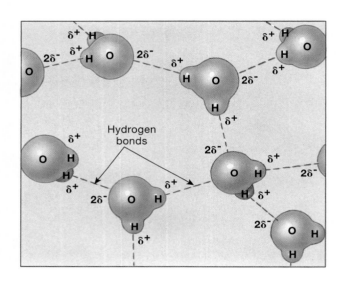

(a) Formation of
water molecule

•**FIGURE 2-5** Polar Covalent Bonds and the Structure
of Water

(b) Charges on a
water molecule

•**FIGURE 2-6** Hydrogen Bonds

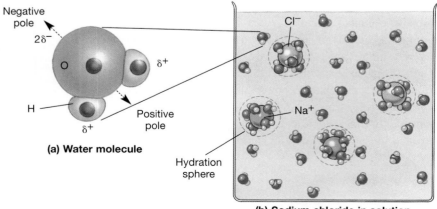

(a) Water molecule

(b) Sodium chloride in solution

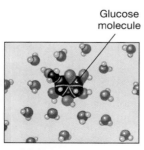

(c) Glucose in solution

•**FIGURE 2-8** Water Molecules and Solutions

NOTES
_____

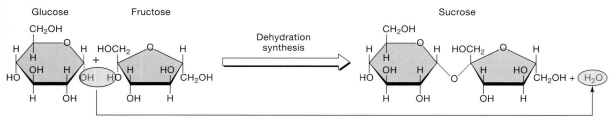

(a) During dehydration synthesis, two molecules are joined by the removal of a water molecule.

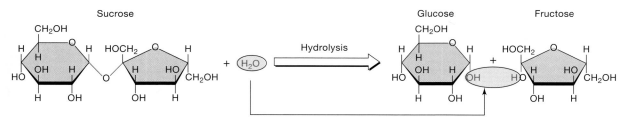

(b) Hydrolysis reverses the steps of dehydration synthesis; a complex
molecule is broken down by the addition of a water molecule.

•FIGURE 2-11 The Formation and Breakdown of Complex Sugars

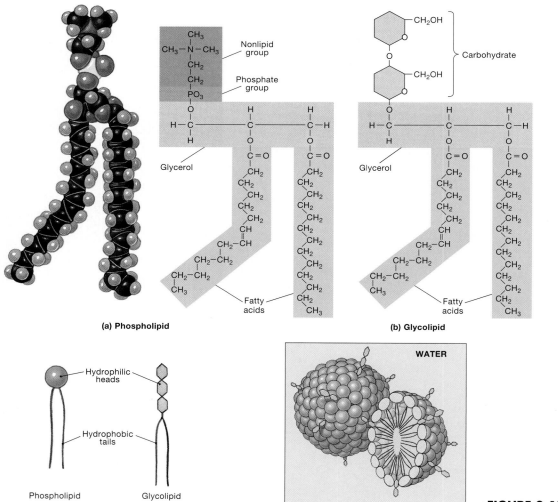

(a) Phospholipid

(b) Glycolipid

(c) Micelle structure

•FIGURE 2-17 Phospholipids
and Glycolipids

NOTES

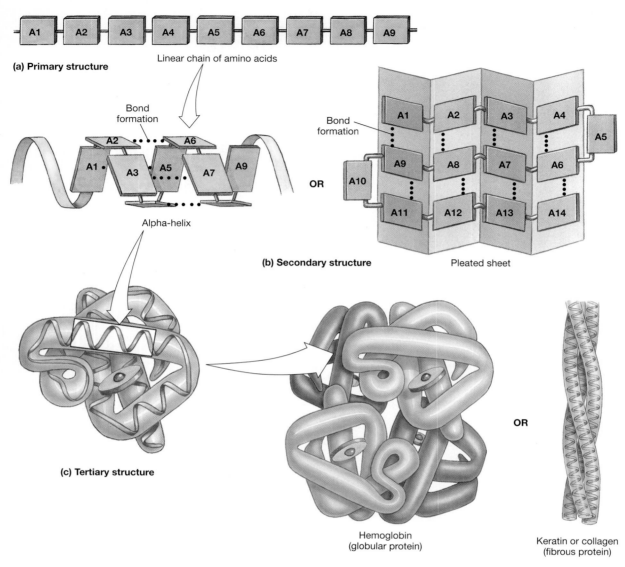

(a) Primary structure

Linear chain of amino acids

Bond formation

Alpha-helix

(b) Secondary structure

Pleated sheet

(c) Tertiary structure

Hemoglobin
(globular protein)

OR

Keratin or collagen
(fibrous protein)

(d) Quaternary structure

•FIGURE 2-20 Protein Structure

NOTES

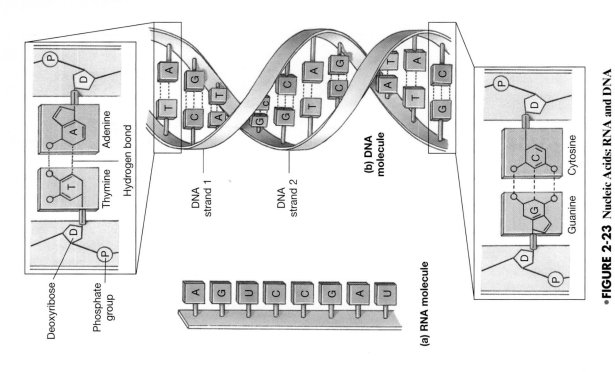

• FIGURE 2-23 Nucleic Acids: RNA and DNA

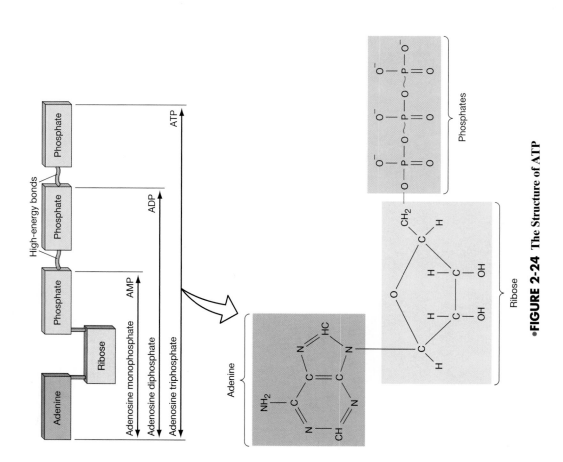

• FIGURE 2-24 The Structure of ATP

NOTES

3   The Cellular Level of Organization

CHAPTER OUTLINE

CHAPTER OBJECTIVES

1. List the functions of the cell membrane and the structural features that enable it to perform those functions.
2. Specify the routes by which different ions and molecules can enter or leave a cell and the factors that may restrict such movement.
3. Describe the various transport mechanisms that cells use to facilitate the absorption or removal of specific substances.
4. Explain the origin and significance of the transmembrane potential.
5. Describe the organelles of a typical cell, and indicate the specific functions of each.
6. Explain the functions of the cell nucleus.
7. Discuss the nature and importance of the genetic code.
8. Summarize the process of protein synthesis.
9. Describe the stages of the cell life cycle.
10. Describe the process of mitosis, and explain its significance.
11. Define differentiation, and explain its importance.

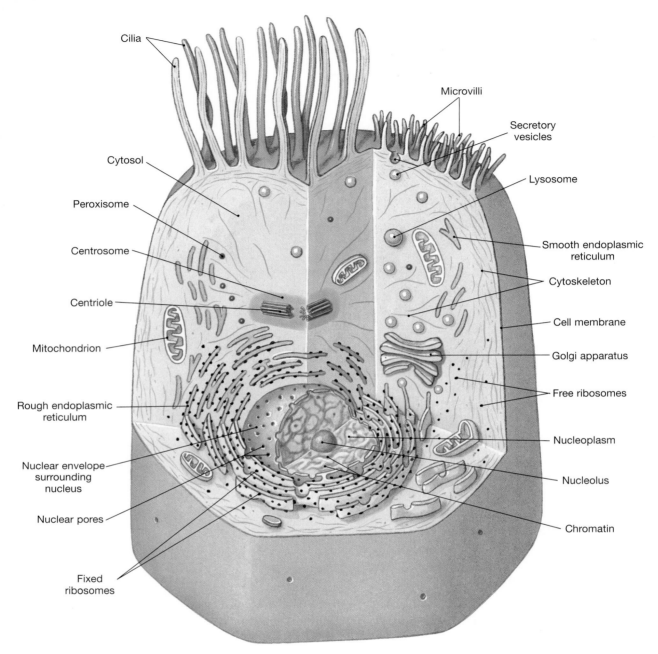

Cilia

Microvilli

Secretory
vesicles

Cytosol

Lysosome

Peroxisome

Smooth endoplasmic
reticulum

Centrosome

Cytoskeleton

Centriole

Cell membrane

Mitochondrion

Golgi apparatus

Rough endoplasmic
reticulum

Free ribosomes

Nucleoplasm

Nuclear envelope
surrounding
nucleus

Nucleolus

Nuclear pores

Chromatin

Fixed
ribosomes

•FIGURE 3-2 The Anatomy of a Representative Cell

NOTES

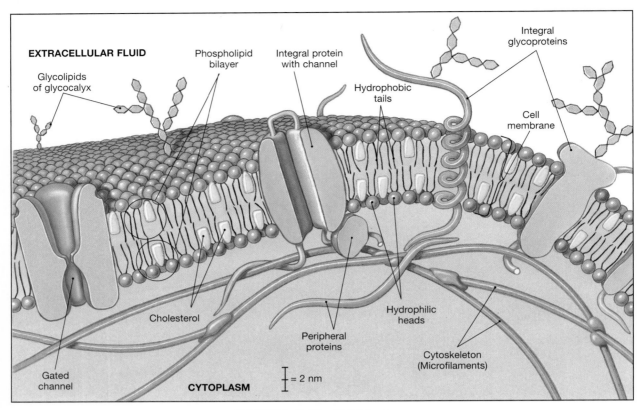

•FIGURE 3-3 The Cell Membrane

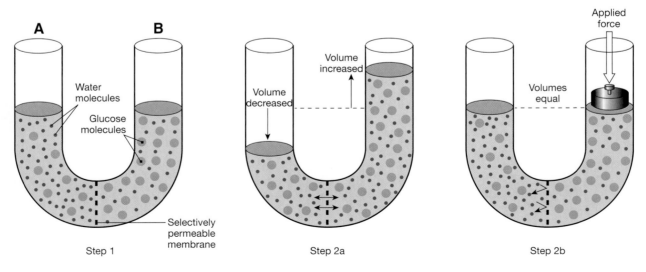

•FIGURE 3-7 Osmosis

NOTES

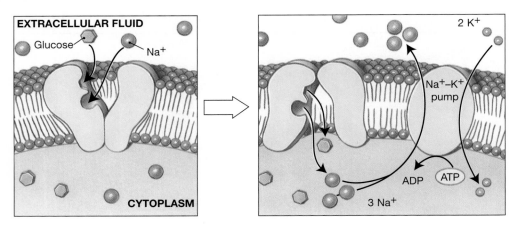

•FIGURE 3-11 Secondary Active Transport

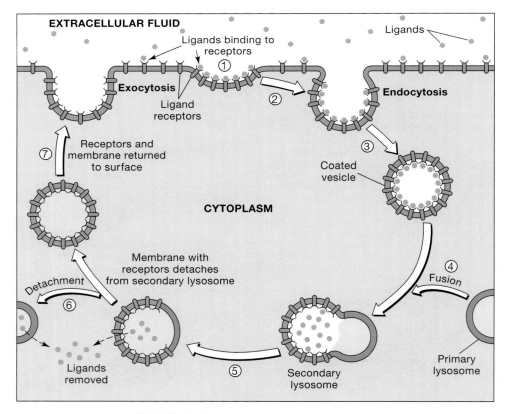

•FIGURE 3-12 Receptor-Mediated Endocytosis

NOTES

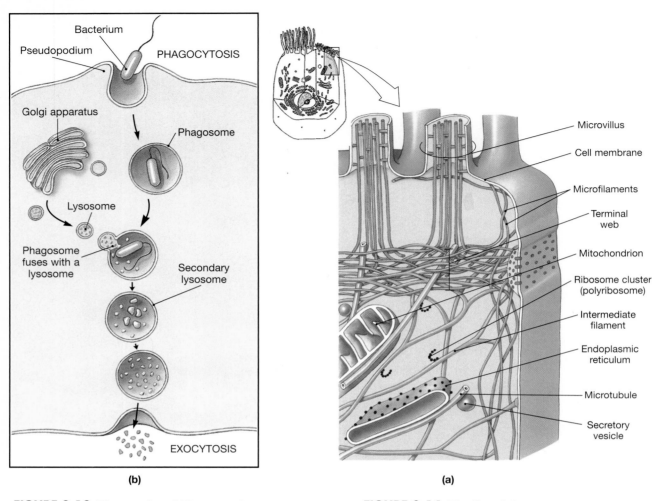

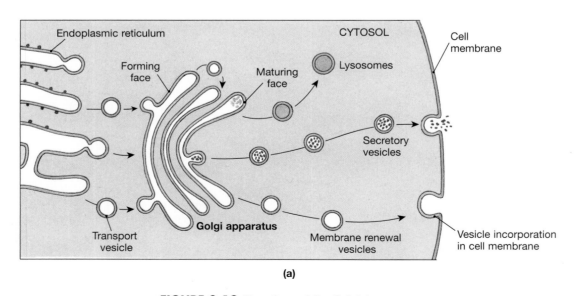

•**FIGURE 3-13** Pinocytosis and Phagocytosis

•**FIGURE 3-14** The Cytoskeleton

•**FIGURE 3-19** Functions of the Golgi Apparatus

NOTES

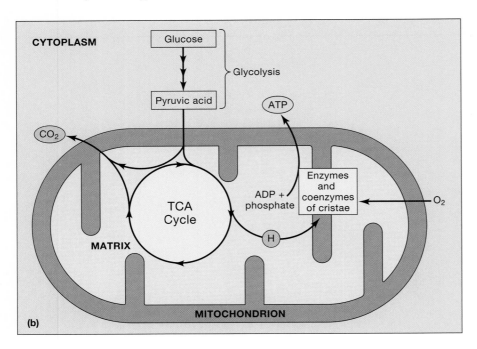

•FIGURE 3-20 Mitochondria

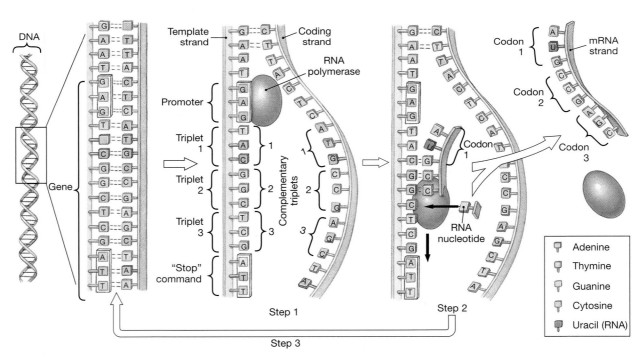

•FIGURE 3-23 mRNA Transcription

NOTES

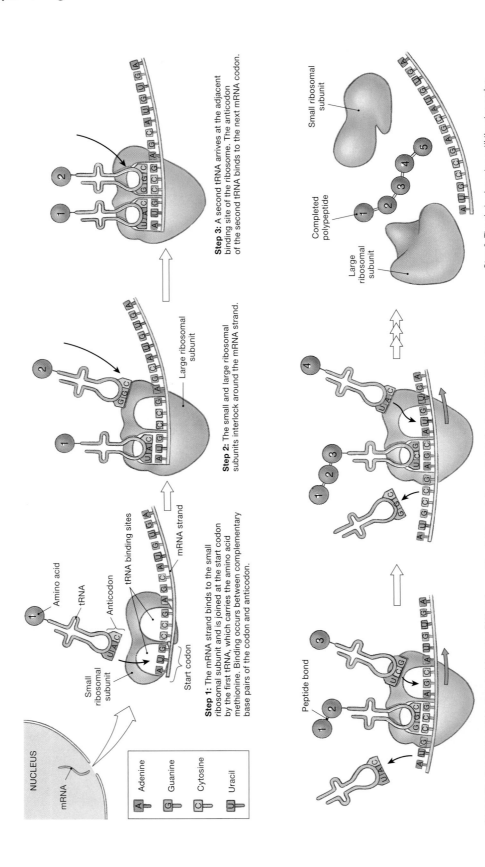

Step 1: The mRNA strand binds to the small ribosomal subunit and is joined at the start codon by the first tRNA, which carries the amino acid methionine. Binding occurs between complementary base pairs of the codon and anticodon.

Step 2: The small and large ribosomal subunits interlock around the mRNA strand.

Step 3: A second tRNA arrives at the adjacent binding site of the ribosome. The anticodon of the second tRNA binds to the next mRNA codon.

Step 4: The first amino acid is detached from its tRNA and is joined to the second amino acid by a peptide bond. The ribosome moves one codon farther along the mRNA strand; the first tRNA detaches as another tRNA arrives.

Step 5: This cycle is repeated as the ribosome moves along the length of the mRNA strand, binds new tRNAs, and incorporates their amino acids into the polypeptide chain.

Step 6: The chain elongates until the stop codon is reached; the components then separate.

•FIGURE 3-25 The Process of Translation

NOTES

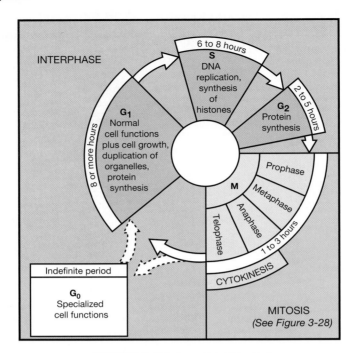

•FIGURE 3-26 The Cell Life Cycle

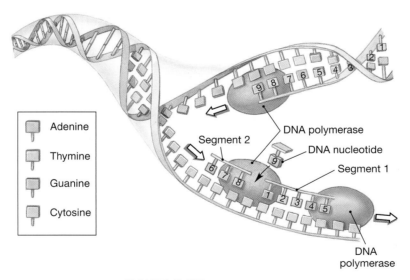

•FIGURE 3-27 DNA Replication

NOTES

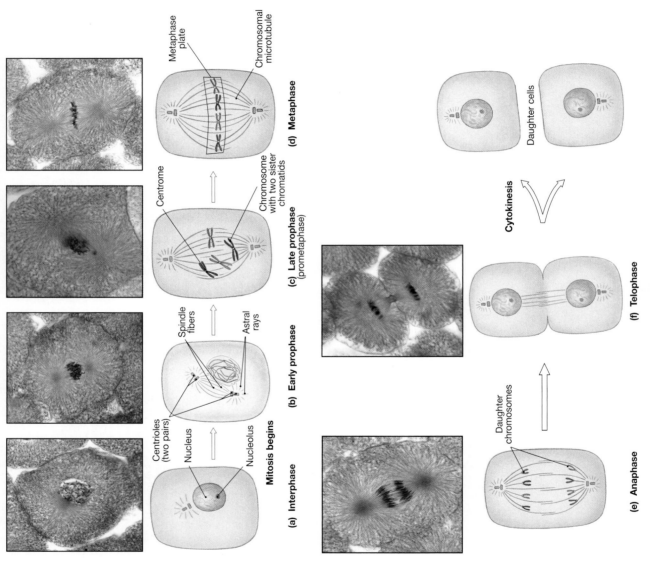

•FIGURE 3-28
Interphase, Mitosis, and
Cytokinesis

(a) Interphase

Mitosis begins

(b) Early prophase

(c) Late prophase (prometaphase)

(d) Metaphase

(e) Anaphase

Cytokinesis

(f) Telophase

Centrioles (two pairs)

Nucleus

Nucleolus

Spindle fibers

Astral rays

Centrome

Chromosome with two sister chromatids

Metaphase plate

Chromosomal microtubule

Daughter chromosomes

Daughter cells

NOTES

4   The Tissue Level of Organization

CHAPTER OUTLINE

CHAPTER OBJECTIVES

1. Identify the four major tissue types of the body and their roles.
2. Discuss the types and functions of epithelial cells.
3. Describe the relationship between form and function for each epithelial type.
4. Compare the structures and functions of the various types of connective tissues.
5. Explain how epithelial and connective tissues combine to form four types of membranes, and specify the functions of each.
6. Describe how connective tissue establishes the framework of the body.
7. Describe the three types of muscle tissue and the special structural features of each type.
8. Discuss the basic structure and role of neural tissue.
9. Describe how injuries and aging affect the tissues of the body.

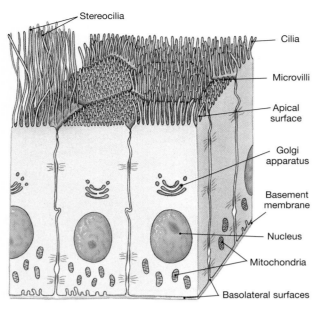

•**FIGURE 4-1** The Polarity of Epithelial Cells

Stereocilia
Cilia
Microvilli
Apical surface
Golgi apparatus
Basement membrane
Nucleus
Mitochondria
Basolateral surfaces

•**FIGURE 4-2** Intercellular Connections

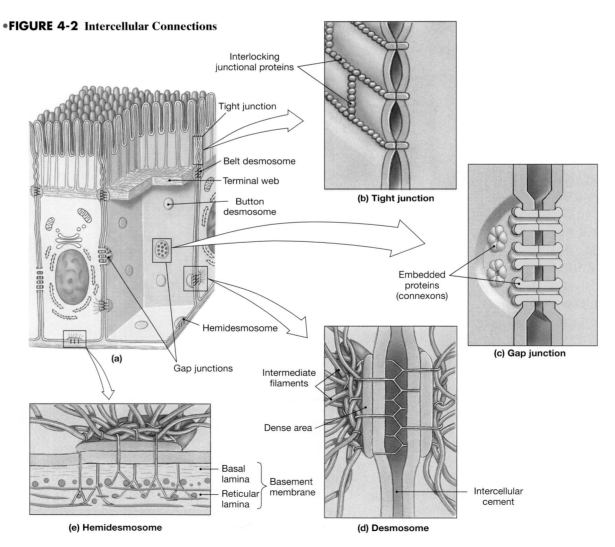

Interlocking junctional proteins

Tight junction

Belt desmosome

Terminal web

Button desmosome

(b) Tight junction

Embedded proteins (connexons)

(c) Gap junction

Hemidesmosome

Gap junctions

(a)

Intermediate filaments

Dense area

Basal lamina
Reticular lamina
Basement membrane

Intercellular cement

(e) Hemidesmosome

(d) Desmosome

© 2002 Prentice Hall, Inc.

NOTES

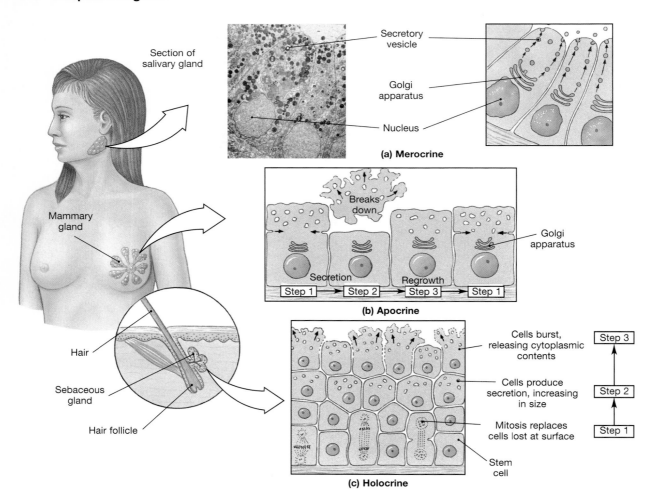

Secretory vesicle

Golgi apparatus

Nucleus

(a) Merocrine

Section of salivary gland

Mammary gland

Hair

Sebaceous gland

Hair follicle

Breaks down

Secretion

Regrowth

Step 1 → Step 2 → Step 3 → Step 1

Golgi apparatus

(b) Apocrine

Cells burst, releasing cytoplasmic contents

Cells produce secretion, increasing in size

Mitosis replaces cells lost at surface

Stem cell

Step 3

Step 2

Step 1

(c) Holocrine

•FIGURE 4-6 Mechanisms of Glandular Secretion

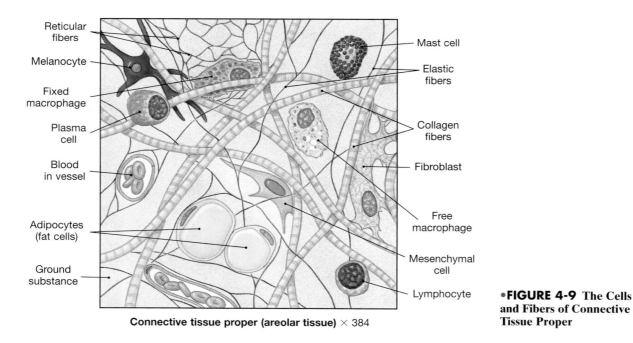

Reticular fibers

Melanocyte

Fixed macrophage

Plasma cell

Blood in vessel

Adipocytes (fat cells)

Ground substance

Mast cell

Elastic fibers

Collagen fibers

Fibroblast

Free macrophage

Mesenchymal cell

Lymphocyte

Connective tissue proper (areolar tissue) × 384

•FIGURE 4-9 The Cells and Fibers of Connective Tissue Proper

NOTES

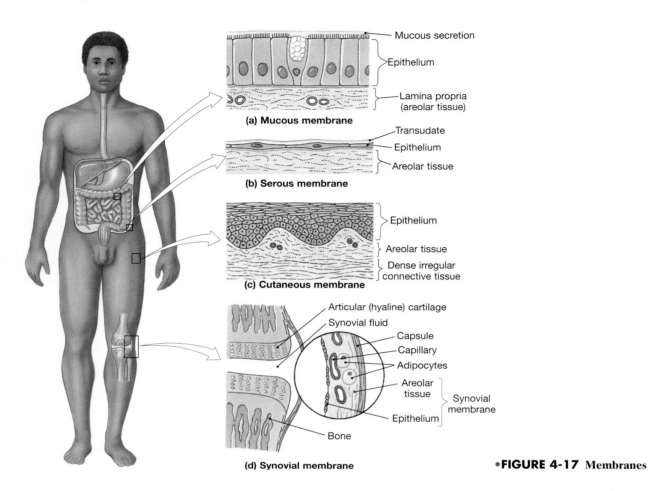

(a) Mucous membrane

(b) Serous membrane

(c) Cutaneous membrane

(d) Synovial membrane

•**FIGURE 4-17** Membranes

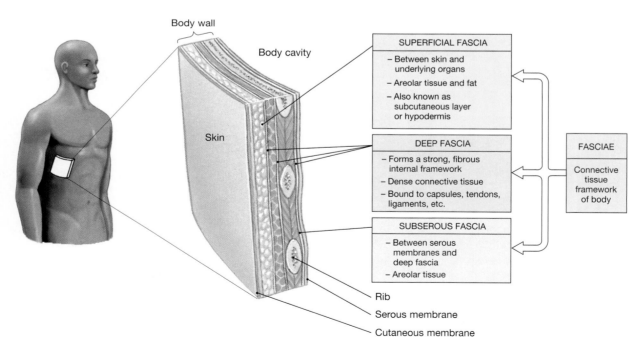

•**FIGURE 4-18** The Fasciae

© 2002 Prentice Hall, Inc.

NOTES

5   The Integumentary System

CHAPTER OUTLINE

CHAPTER OBJECTIVES

1. Describe the main structural features of the epidermis, and explain their functional significance.
2. Explain what accounts for individual and racial differences in skin, such as skin color.
3. Discuss the effects of ultraviolet radiation on the skin and the role played by melanocytes.
4. Describe the structure and functions of the dermis.
5. Describe the structure and functions of the subcutaneous layer.
6. Explain the mechanisms that produce hair, and determine hair texture and color.
7. Discuss the various kinds of glands in the skin and the secretions of those glands.
8. Explain how the sweat glands of the integumentary system play a major role in regulating body temperature.
9. Describe the anatomical structure of nails and how they are formed.
10. Explain how the skin responds to injury and repairs itself.
11. Summarize the effects of the aging process on the skin.
12. Give examples of interactions between the integumentary system and each of the other organ systems.

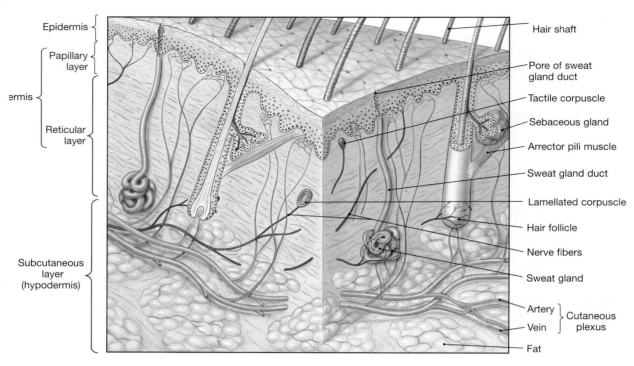

•**FIGURE 5-1** The Components of the Integumentary System

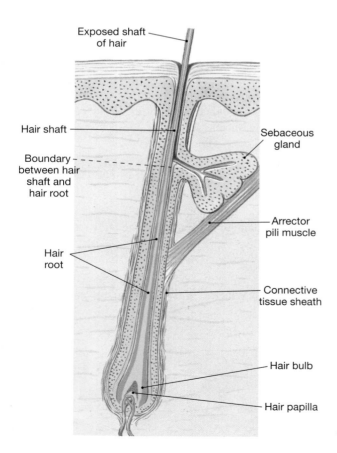

•**FIGURE 5-6** The Anatomy of a Single Hair

NOTES

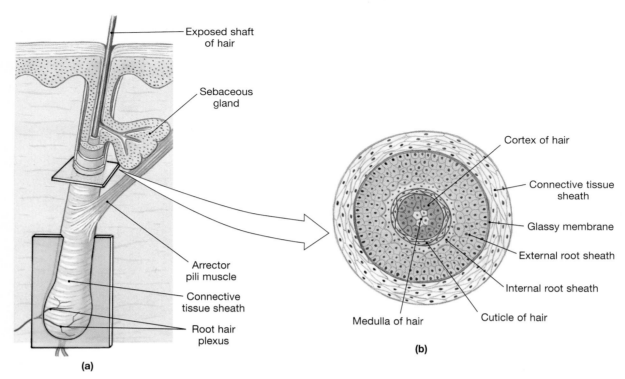

(a)

(b)

•FIGURE 5-7 Hair Follicles

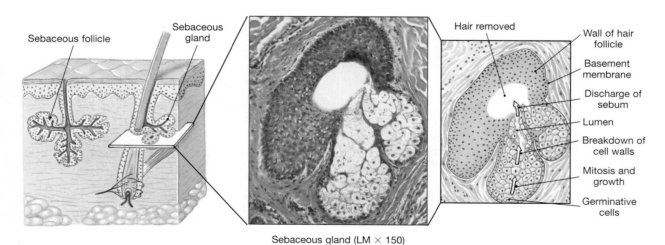

Sebaceous gland (LM × 150)

•FIGURE 5-8 Sebaceous Glands and Follicles

NOTES

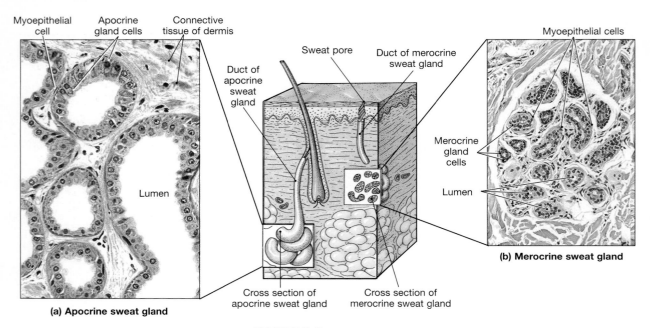

Myoepithelial cell   Apocrine gland cells   Connective tissue of dermis

Lumen

(a) Apocrine sweat gland

Sweat pore   Duct of merocrine sweat gland

Duct of apocrine sweat gland

Myoepithelial cells

Merocrine gland cells

Lumen

Cross section of apocrine sweat gland

Cross section of merocrine sweat gland

(b) Merocrine sweat gland

•FIGURE 5-9 Sweat Glands

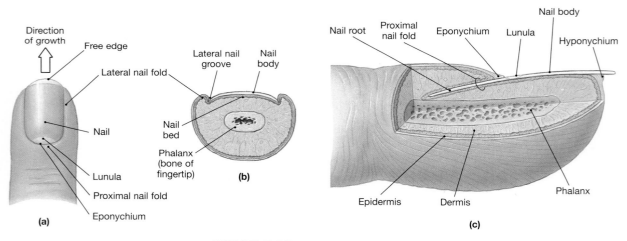

Direction of growth

Free edge

Lateral nail fold

Nail

Lunula

Proximal nail fold

Eponychium

(a)

Lateral nail groove   Nail body

Nail bed

Phalanx (bone of fingertip)

(b)

Nail root   Proximal nail fold   Eponychium   Lunula   Nail body

Hyponychium

Epidermis   Dermis   Phalanx

(c)

•FIGURE 5-10 The Structure of a Nail

NOTES

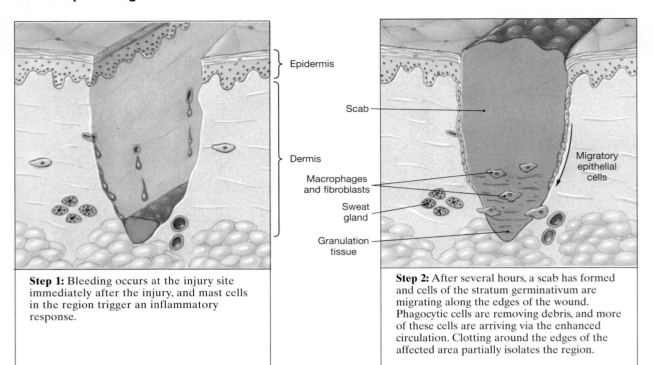

Step 1: Bleeding occurs at the injury site immediately after the injury, and mast cells in the region trigger an inflammatory response.

Step 2: After several hours, a scab has formed and cells of the stratum germinativum are migrating along the edges of the wound. Phagocytic cells are removing debris, and more of these cells are arriving via the enhanced circulation. Clotting around the edges of the affected area partially isolates the region.

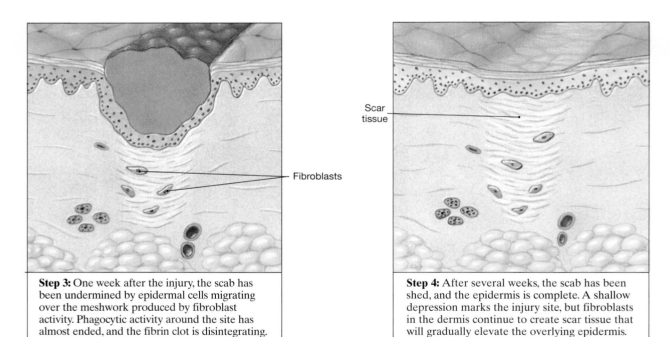

Step 3: One week after the injury, the scab has been undermined by epidermal cells migrating over the meshwork produced by fibroblast activity. Phagocytic activity around the site has almost ended, and the fibrin clot is disintegrating.

Step 4: After several weeks, the scab has been shed, and the epidermis is complete. A shallow depression marks the injury site, but fibroblasts in the dermis continue to create scar tissue that will gradually elevate the overlying epidermis.

•**FIGURE 5-11** Integumentary Repair

NOTES

6 Osseous Tissue and Skeletal Structure

CHAPTER OUTLINE

CHAPTER OBJECTIVES

1. Describe the functions of the skeletal system.
2. Classify bones according to their shapes and internal organization, and give examples of each type.
3. Identify the cell types in bone, and list their major functions.
4. Compare the structures and functions of compact bone and spongy bone.
5. Compare the mechanisms of intramembranous ossification and endochondral ossification.
6. Discuss the timing of bone development and growth, and account for the differences in the internal structure of the bones of adults.
7. Describe the remodeling and homeostatic mechanisms of the skeletal system.
8. Discuss the effects of nutrition, hormones, exercise, and aging on bone development and on the skeletal system.
9. Describe the types of fractures, and explain how they heal.
10. Identify the major types of bone markings, and explain their functional significance.
11. Give examples of interactions between the skeletal system and each of the other organ systems.

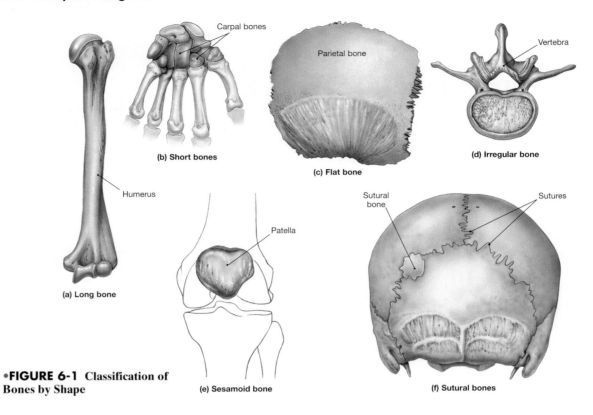

•**FIGURE 6-1** Classification of
Bones by Shape

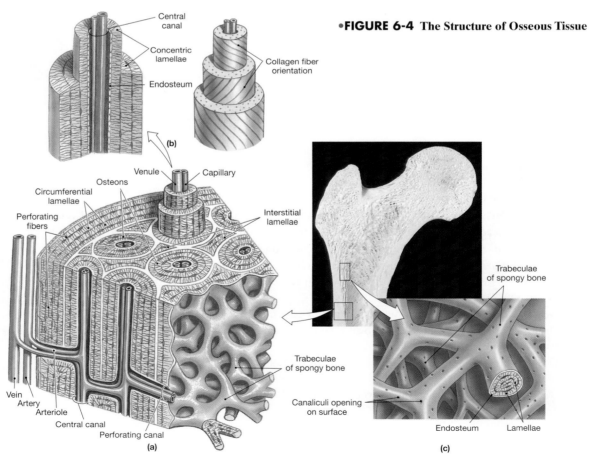

•**FIGURE 6-4** The Structure of Osseous Tissue

NOTES

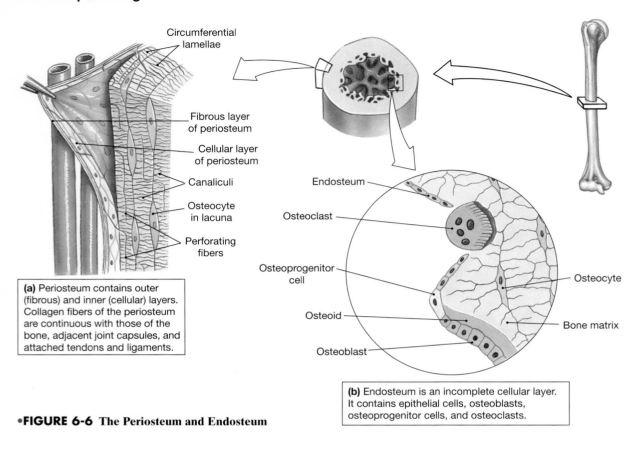

Circumferential
lamellae

Fibrous layer
of periosteum

Cellular layer
of periosteum

Canaliculi

Osteocyte
in lacuna

Perforating
fibers

(a) Periosteum contains outer
(fibrous) and inner (cellular) layers.
Collagen fibers of the periosteum
are continuous with those of the
bone, adjacent joint capsules, and
attached tendons and ligaments.

Endosteum

Osteoclast

Osteoprogenitor
cell

Osteoid

Osteoblast

Osteocyte

Bone matrix

(b) Endosteum is an incomplete cellular layer.
It contains epithelial cells, osteoblasts,
osteoprogenitor cells, and osteoclasts.

•FIGURE 6-6 The Periosteum and Endosteum

•FIGURE 6-7 Intramembranous Ossification

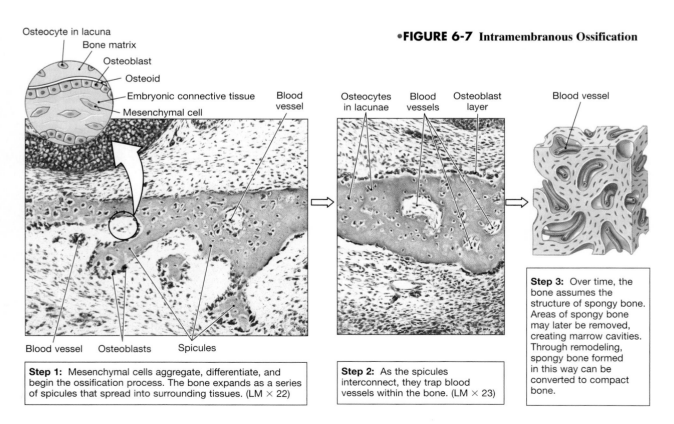

Osteocyte in lacuna
Bone matrix
Osteoblast
Osteoid
Embryonic connective tissue
Mesenchymal cell

Blood
vessel

Osteocytes
in lacunae

Blood
vessels

Osteoblast
layer

Blood vessel

Blood vessel   Osteoblasts   Spicules

Step 1: Mesenchymal cells aggregate, differentiate, and
begin the ossification process. The bone expands as a series
of spicules that spread into surrounding tissues. (LM × 22)

Step 2: As the spicules
interconnect, they trap blood
vessels within the bone. (LM × 23)

Step 3: Over time, the
bone assumes the
structure of spongy bone.
Areas of spongy bone
may later be removed,
creating marrow cavities.
Through remodeling,
spongy bone formed
in this way can be
converted to compact
bone.

NOTES

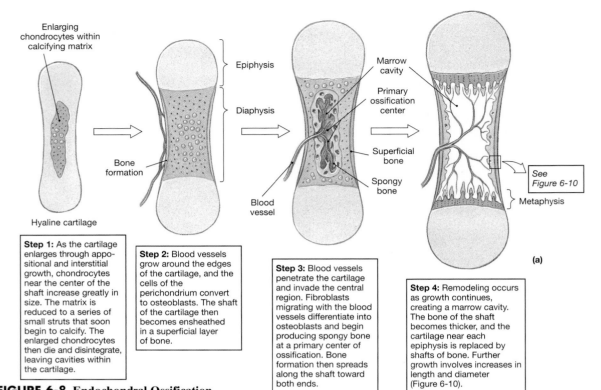

Enlarging chondrocytes within calcifying matrix

Hyaline cartilage

Bone formation

Epiphysis

Diaphysis

Blood vessel

Marrow cavity

Primary ossification center

Superficial bone

Spongy bone

See Figure 6-10

Metaphysis

(a)

Step 1: As the cartilage enlarges through appositional and interstitial growth, chondrocytes near the center of the shaft increase greatly in size. The matrix is reduced to a series of small struts that soon begin to calcify. The enlarged chondrocytes then die and disintegrate, leaving cavities within the cartilage.

Step 2: Blood vessels grow around the edges of the cartilage, and the cells of the perichondrium convert to osteoblasts. The shaft of the cartilage then becomes ensheathed in a superficial layer of bone.

Step 3: Blood vessels penetrate the cartilage and invade the central region. Fibroblasts migrating with the blood vessels differentiate into osteoblasts and begin producing spongy bone at a primary center of ossification. Bone formation then spreads along the shaft toward both ends.

Step 4: Remodeling occurs as growth continues, creating a marrow cavity. The bone of the shaft becomes thicker, and the cartilage near each epiphysis is replaced by shafts of bone. Further growth involves increases in length and diameter (Figure 6-10).

•**FIGURE 6-8** Endochondral Ossification

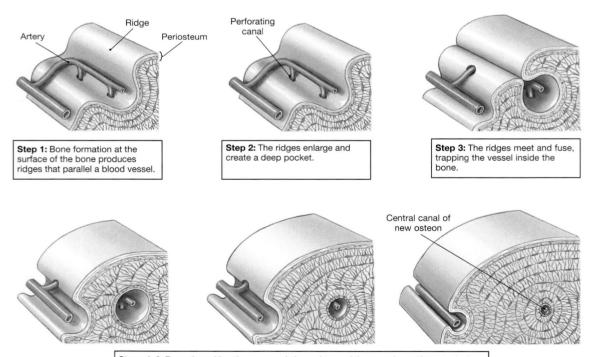

Artery

Ridge

Periosteum

Perforating canal

Central canal of new osteon

Step 1: Bone formation at the surface of the bone produces ridges that parallel a blood vessel.

Step 2: The ridges enlarge and create a deep pocket.

Step 3: The ridges meet and fuse, trapping the vessel inside the bone.

Steps 4–6: Bone deposition then proceeds inward toward the vessel, creating a typical osteon. Meanwhile, additional circumferential lamellae are deposited and the bone continues to increase in diameter. As it does so, additional blood vessels will be enclosed.

(a) Steps in appositional bone growth

•**FIGURE 6-10** Appositional Bone Growth

NOTES

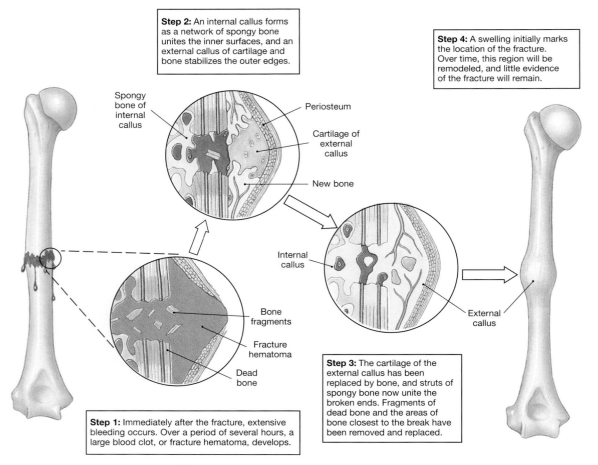

Step 2: An internal callus forms as a network of spongy bone unites the inner surfaces, and an external callus of cartilage and bone stabilizes the outer edges.

Step 4: A swelling initially marks the location of the fracture. Over time, this region will be remodeled, and little evidence of the fracture will remain.

Spongy bone of internal callus

Periosteum

Cartilage of external callus

New bone

Internal callus

External callus

Bone fragments

Fracture hematoma

Dead bone

Step 3: The cartilage of the external callus has been replaced by bone, and struts of spongy bone now unite the broken ends. Fragments of dead bone and the areas of bone closest to the break have been removed and replaced.

Step 1: Immediately after the fracture, extensive bleeding occurs. Over a period of several hours, a large blood clot, or fracture hematoma, develops.

•FIGURE 6-14 Steps in the Repair of a Fracture

NOTES

7   The Axial Skeleton

CHAPTER OUTLINE

CHAPTER OBJECTIVES

1. Identify the bones of the axial skeleton, and specify their functions.
2. Identify the bones of the cranium and face, and explain the significance of the markings on the individual bones.
3. Describe the structure of the nasal complex and the functions of the individual bones.
4. Explain the functions of the paranasal sinuses.
5. Describe key structural differences among the skulls of infants, children, and adults.
6. Identify and describe the curvatures of the spinal column and their functions.
7. Identify the vertebral regions, and describe the distinctive structural and functional characteristics of each vertebral group.
8. Explain the significance of the articulations between the thoracic vertebrae and ribs and between the ribs and sternum.

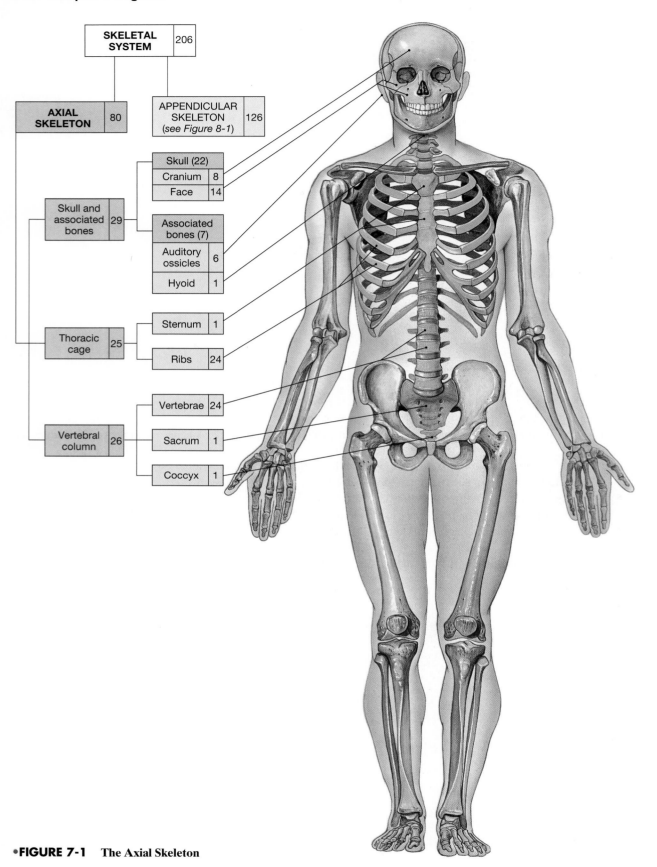

•**FIGURE 7-1**   **The Axial Skeleton**

NOTES

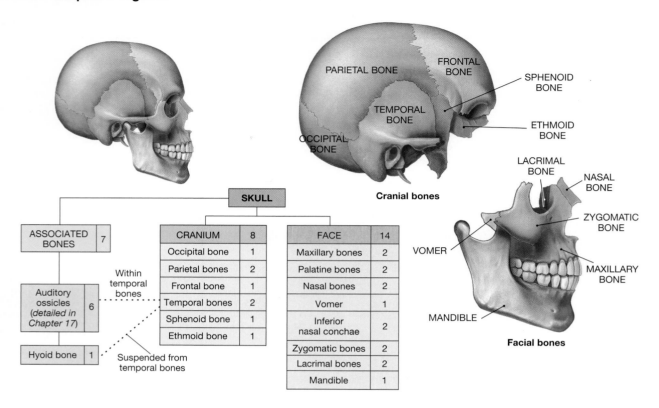

Cranial bones

Facial bones

•**FIGURE 7-2** Cranial and Facial Subdivisions of the Skull

NOTES

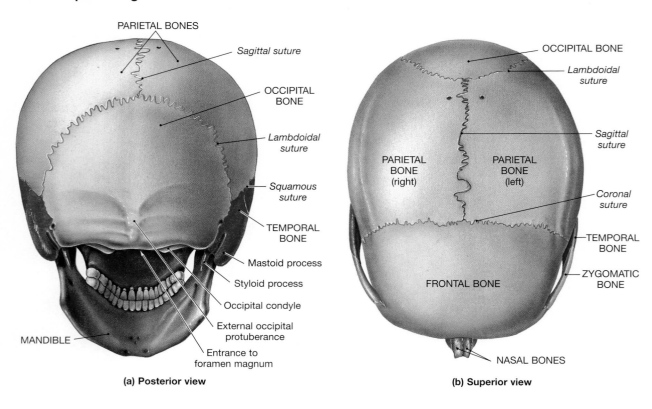

PARIETAL BONES

Sagittal suture

OCCIPITAL BONE

Lambdoidal suture

Squamous suture

TEMPORAL BONE

Mastoid process

Styloid process

Occipital condyle

External occipital protuberance

Entrance to foramen magnum

MANDIBLE

(a) Posterior view

OCCIPITAL BONE

Lambdoidal suture

Sagittal suture

PARIETAL BONE (right)

PARIETAL BONE (left)

Coronal suture

TEMPORAL BONE

ZYGOMATIC BONE

FRONTAL BONE

NASAL BONES

(b) Superior view

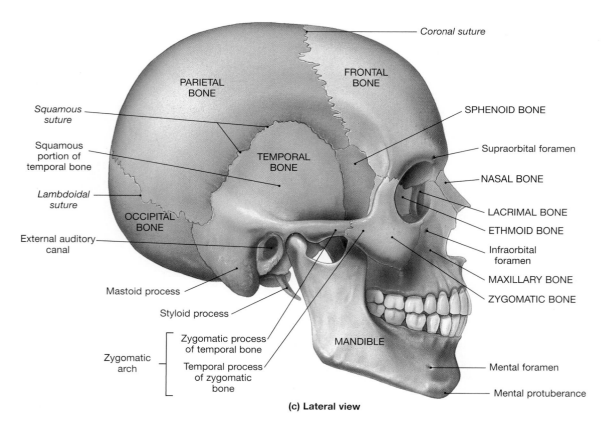

Coronal suture

PARIETAL BONE

FRONTAL BONE

SPHENOID BONE

Squamous suture

Squamous portion of temporal bone

TEMPORAL BONE

Supraorbital foramen

NASAL BONE

LACRIMAL BONE

ETHMOID BONE

Lambdoidal suture

OCCIPITAL BONE

Infraorbital foramen

MAXILLARY BONE

ZYGOMATIC BONE

External auditory canal

Mastoid process

Styloid process

Zygomatic arch

Zygomatic process of temporal bone

Temporal process of zygomatic bone

MANDIBLE

Mental foramen

Mental protuberance

(c) Lateral view

•FIGURE 7-3 The Adult Skull

© 2002 Prentice Hall, Inc.

NOTES

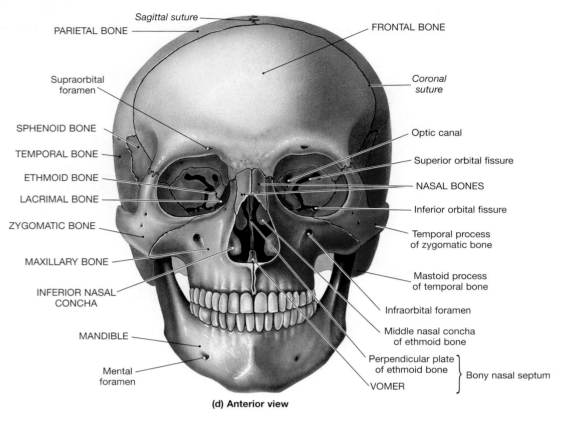

PARIETAL BONE

Sagittal suture

FRONTAL BONE

Supraorbital foramen

Coronal suture

SPHENOID BONE

TEMPORAL BONE

ETHMOID BONE

LACRIMAL BONE

ZYGOMATIC BONE

MAXILLARY BONE

INFERIOR NASAL CONCHA

MANDIBLE

Mental foramen

Optic canal

Superior orbital fissure

NASAL BONES

Inferior orbital fissure

Temporal process of zygomatic bone

Mastoid process of temporal bone

Infraorbital foramen

Middle nasal concha of ethmoid bone

Perpendicular plate of ethmoid bone

VOMER

Bony nasal septum

(d) Anterior view

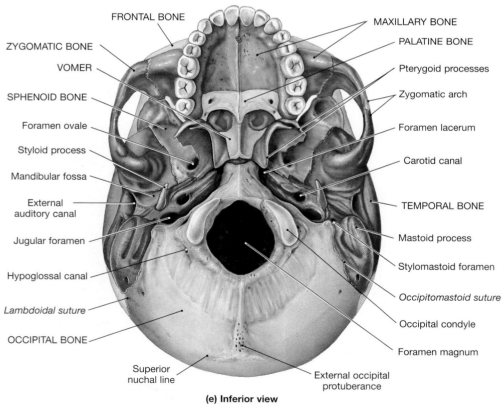

FRONTAL BONE

ZYGOMATIC BONE

VOMER

SPHENOID BONE

Foramen ovale

Styloid process

Mandibular fossa

External auditory canal

Jugular foramen

Hypoglossal canal

Lambdoidal suture

OCCIPITAL BONE

Superior nuchal line

MAXILLARY BONE

PALATINE BONE

Pterygoid processes

Zygomatic arch

Foramen lacerum

Carotid canal

TEMPORAL BONE

Mastoid process

Stylomastoid foramen

Occipitomastoid suture

Occipital condyle

Foramen magnum

External occipital protuberance

(e) Inferior view

•FIGURE 7-3 The Adult Skull *(continued)*

NOTES
_____

✱ Glabella - single bony prominence of the frontal
bone located between the superciliary arches
in the inferior part of the frontal bone above
the root of the nose.

•FIGURE 7-4 The
Sectional Anatomy of
the Skull

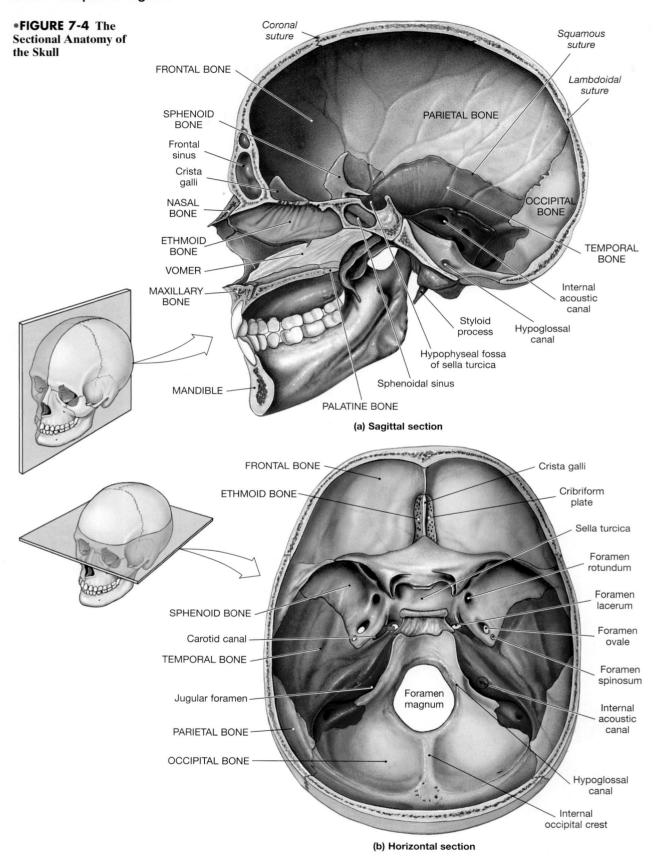

(a) Sagittal section

(b) Horizontal section

NOTES

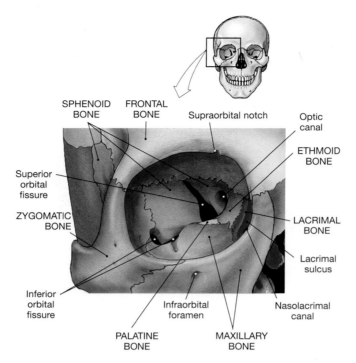

SPHENOID
BONE

FRONTAL
BONE

Supraorbital notch

Optic
canal

ETHMOID
BONE

Superior
orbital
fissure

ZYGOMATIC
BONE

LACRIMAL
BONE

Lacrimal
sulcus

Inferior
orbital
fissure

Infraorbital
foramen

Nasolacrimal
canal

PALATINE
BONE

MAXILLARY
BONE

•FIGURE 7-13 The Orbital Complex

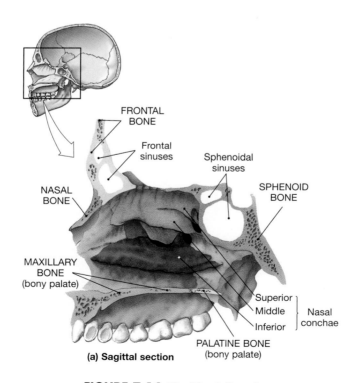

FRONTAL
BONE

Frontal
sinuses

Sphenoidal
sinuses

SPHENOID
BONE

NASAL
BONE

MAXILLARY
BONE
(bony palate)

Superior

Middle

Inferior

Nasal
conchae

PALATINE BONE
(bony palate)

(a) Sagittal section

•FIGURE 7-14 The Nasal Complex

NOTES

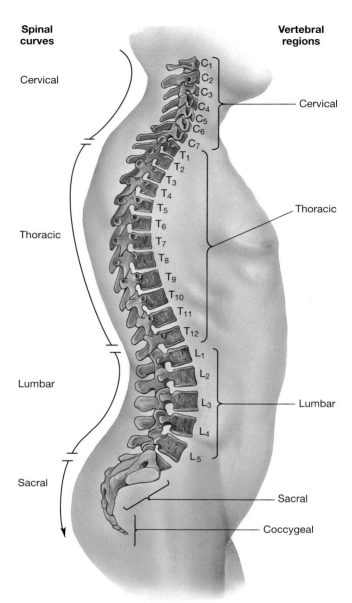

Spinal curves

Cervical

Thoracic

Lumbar

Sacral

Vertebral regions

Cervical

Thoracic

Lumbar

Sacral

Coccygeal

C1
C2
C3
C4
C5
C6
C7

T1
T2
T3
T4
T5
T6
T7
T8
T9
T10
T11
T12

L1
L2
L3
L4
L5

•**FIGURE 7-16** The Vertebral Column

NOTES

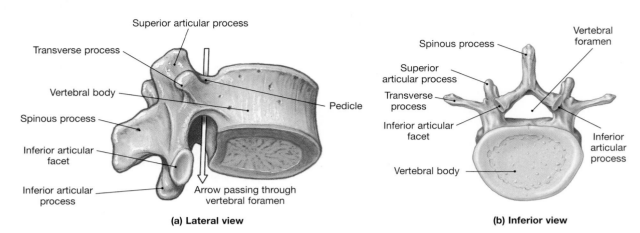

Superior articular process

Transverse process

Vertebral body

Spinous process

Inferior articular facet

Inferior articular process

Pedicle

Arrow passing through vertebral foramen

(a) Lateral view

Spinous process

Vertebral foramen

Superior articular process

Transverse process

Inferior articular facet

Vertebral body

Inferior articular process

(b) Inferior view

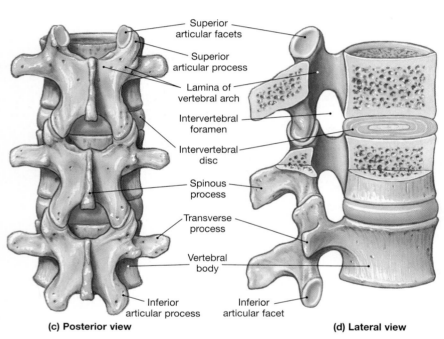

Superior articular facets

Superior articular process

Lamina of vertebral arch

Intervertebral foramen

Intervertebral disc

Spinous process

Transverse process

Vertebral body

Inferior articular process

Inferior articular facet

(c) Posterior view

(d) Lateral view

•**FIGURE 7-17** Vertebral Anatomy

NOTES

TABLE 7-2 Regional Differences in Vertebral Structure and Function

Feature	Type (Number)		
	Cervical Vertebrae (7)	Thoracic Vertebrae (12)	Lumbar Vertebrae (5)
Location	Neck	Chest	Inferior portion of back
Body	Small, oval, curved faces	Medium, heart-shaped, flat faces; facets for rib articulations	Massive, oval, flat faces
Vertebral foramen	Large	Smaller	Smallest
Spinous process	Long; split tip; points inferiorly	Long, slender; not split; points inferiorly	Blunt, broad, points posteriorly
Transverse process	Has transverse foramen	All but two (T_{11}, T_{12}) have facets for rib articulations	Short; no articular facets or transverse foramen
Functions	Support skull, stabilize relative positions of brain and spinal cord, and allow controlled head movement	Support weight of head, neck, upper limbs, chest; articulate with ribs to allow changes in volume of thoracic cage	Support weight of head, neck, upper limbs, and trunk

NOTES

CHAPTER

8   The Appendicular Skeleton

CHAPTER OUTLINE

CHAPTER OBJECTIVES

1. Identify each bone of the appendicular skeleton.
2. Identify the bones that form the pectoral girdle, their functions, and their superficial features.
3. Identify the bones of the upper limbs, their functions, and their superficial features.
4. Identify the bones that form the pelvic girdle, their functions, and their superficial features.
5. Identify the bones of the lower limbs, their functions, and their superficial features.
6. Discuss structural and functional differences between the pelvis of females and that of males.
7. Explain how study of the skeleton can reveal significant information about an individual.
8. Summarize the skeletal differences between males and females.
9. Briefly describe how the aging process affects the skeletal system.

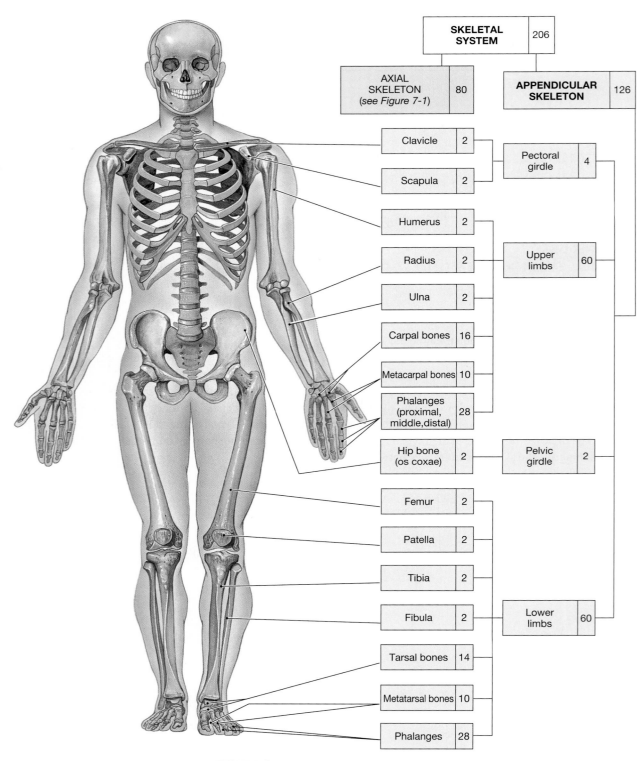

•FIGURE 8-1 The Appendicular Skeleton

NOTES

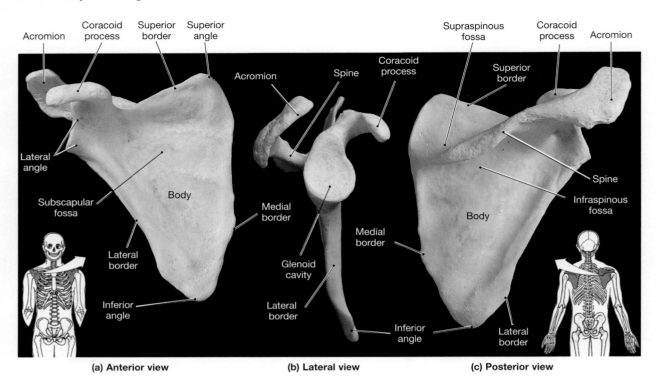

(a) Anterior view   (b) Lateral view   (c) Posterior view

•**FIGURE 8-3** The Scapula

NOTES

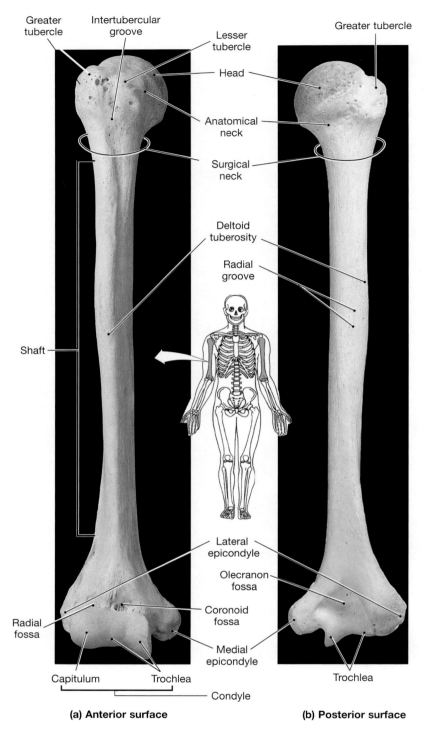

Greater tubercle

Intertubercular groove

Lesser tubercle

Head

Anatomical neck

Surgical neck

Greater tubercle

Deltoid tuberosity

Radial groove

Shaft

Lateral epicondyle

Olecranon fossa

Coronoid fossa

Medial epicondyle

Radial fossa

Capitulum

Trochlea

Condyle

Trochlea

(a) Anterior surface

(b) Posterior surface

•FIGURE 8-4 The Humerus

NOTES

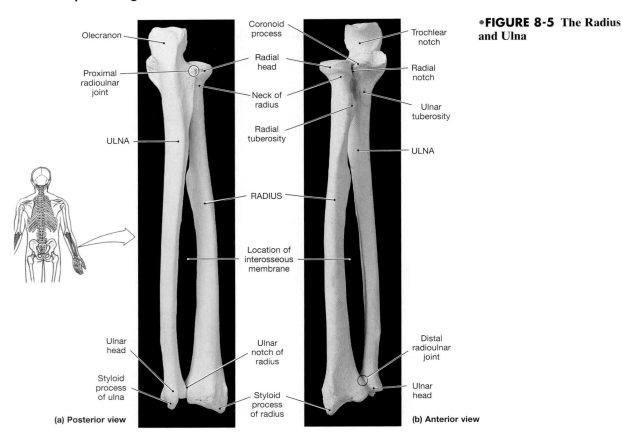

Olecranon

Proximal
radioulnar
joint

ULNA

Coronoid
process

Radial
head

Neck of
radius

Radial
tuberosity

Trochlear
notch

Radial
notch

Ulnar
tuberosity

ULNA

RADIUS

Location of
interosseous
membrane

Ulnar
head

Ulnar
notch of
radius

Distal
radioulnar
joint

Styloid
process
of ulna

Styloid
process
of radius

Ulnar
head

(a) Posterior view

(b) Anterior view

•FIGURE 8-5 The Radius
and Ulna

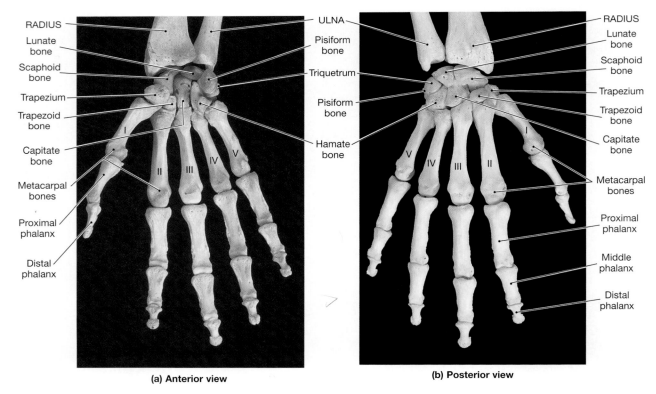

RADIUS

Lunate
bone

Scaphoid
bone

Trapezium

Trapezoid
bone

Capitate
bone

Metacarpal
bones

Proximal
phalanx

Distal
phalanx

ULNA

Pisiform
bone

Triquetrum

Pisiform
bone

Hamate
bone

RADIUS

Lunate
bone

Scaphoid
bone

Trapezium

Trapezoid
bone

Capitate
bone

Metacarpal
bones

Proximal
phalanx

Middle
phalanx

Distal
phalanx

(a) Anterior view

(b) Posterior view

•FIGURE 8-6 Bones of the Wrist and Hand

© 2002 Prentice Hall, Inc.

NOTES

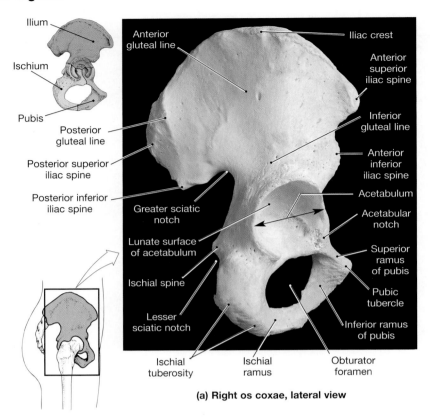

(a) Right os coxae, lateral view

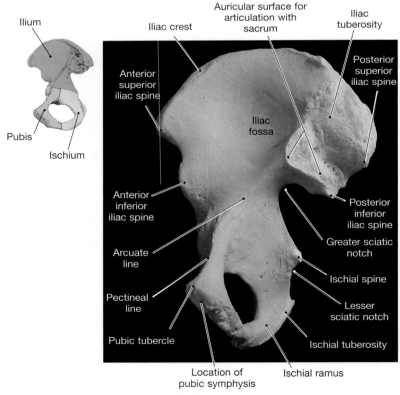

(b) Right os coxae, medial view

•FIGURE 8-7 The Os Coxae

NOTES
_____

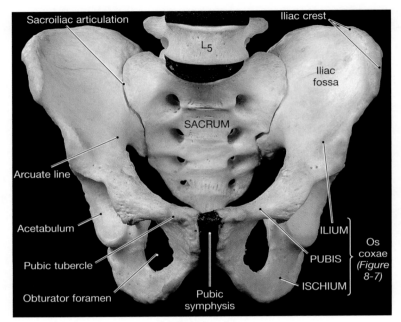

(a) Anterior view

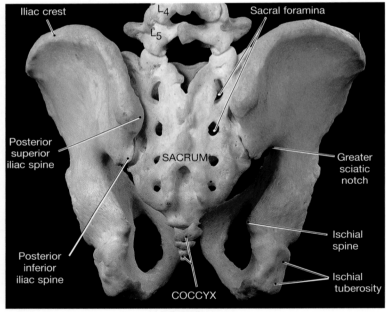

(b) Posterior view

•FIGURE 8-8 The Pelvis

NOTES
_____

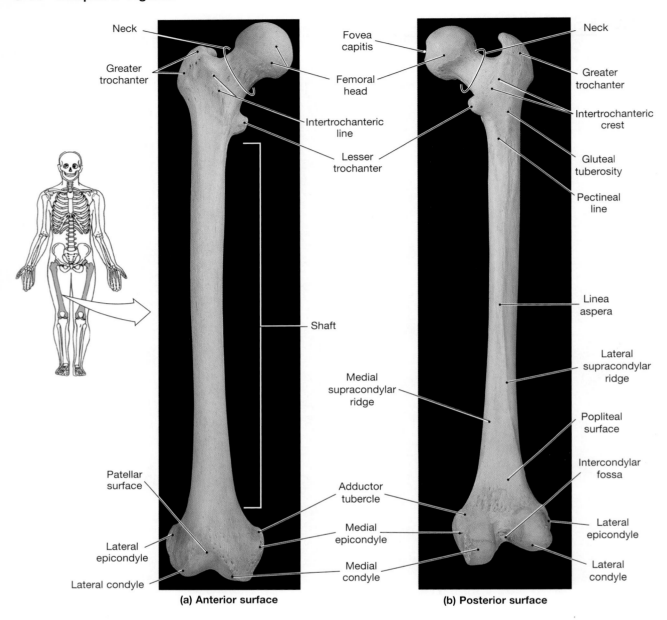

Neck

Greater
trochanter

Fovea
capitis

Femoral
head

Intertrochanteric
line

Lesser
trochanter

Shaft

Medial
supracondylar
ridge

Patellar
surface

Adductor
tubercle

Medial
epicondyle

Lateral
epicondyle

Medial
condyle

Lateral
condyle

(a) Anterior surface

Neck

Greater
trochanter

Intertrochanteric
crest

Gluteal
tuberosity

Pectineal
line

Linea
aspera

Lateral
supracondylar
ridge

Popliteal
surface

Intercondylar
fossa

Lateral
epicondyle

Lateral
condyle

(b) Posterior surface

•**FIGURE 8-11** The Femur

NOTES

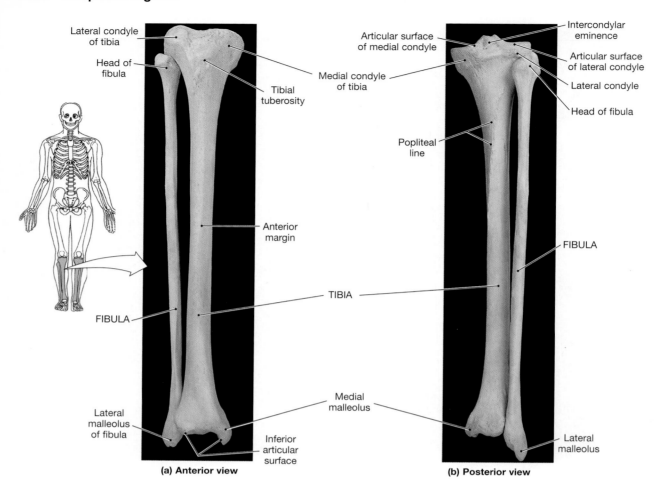

Lateral condyle
of tibia

Head of
fibula

Medial condyle
of tibia

Tibial
tuberosity

Anterior
margin

FIBULA

TIBIA

Lateral
malleolus
of fibula

Medial
malleolus

Inferior
articular
surface

(a) Anterior view

Articular surface
of medial condyle

Intercondylar
eminence

Articular surface
of lateral condyle

Lateral condyle

Head of fibula

Popliteal
line

FIBULA

TIBIA

Lateral
malleolus

(b) Posterior view

•FIGURE 8-13 The Tibia and Fibula

NOTES

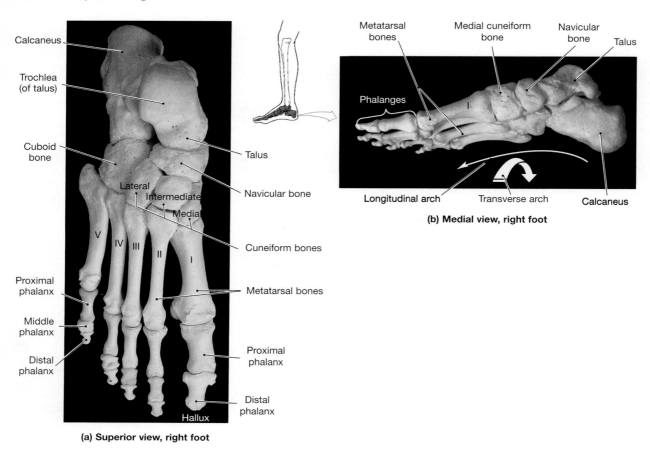

(a) Superior view, right foot

(b) Medial view, right foot

•FIGURE 8-14 Bones of the Ankle and Foot

NOTES

9   **Articulations**

CHAPTER OUTLINE

CHAPTER OBJECTIVES

1. Contrast the major categories of joints, and explain the relationship between structure and function for each category.
2. Describe the basic structure of a synovial joint, identifying possible accessory structures and their functions.
3. Describe the dynamic movements of the skeleton.
4. List the types of synovial joints, and discuss how the characteristic motions of each type are related to its anatomical structure.
5. Describe the articulations between the vertebrae of the vertebral column.
6. Describe the structure and function of the shoulder, elbow, hip, and knee joints.
7. Explain the relationship between joint strength and mobility, using specific examples.

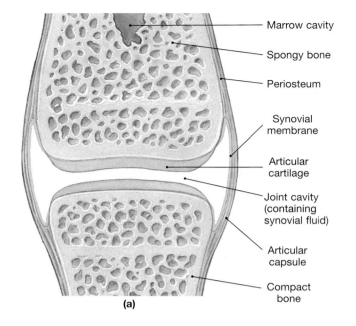

Marrow cavity

Spongy bone

Periosteum

Synovial
membrane

Articular
cartilage

Joint cavity
(containing
synovial fluid)

Articular
capsule

Compact
bone

(a)

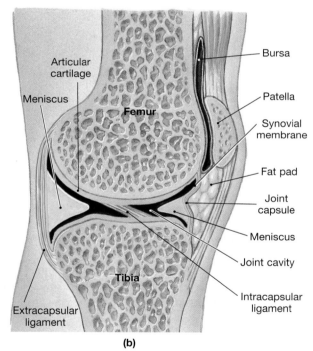

Articular
cartilage

Meniscus

Femur

Bursa

Patella

Synovial
membrane

Fat pad

Joint
capsule

Meniscus

Joint cavity

Intracapsular
ligament

Extracapsular
ligament

Tibia

(b)

•FIGURE 9-1 The Structure of a Synovial Joint

NOTES

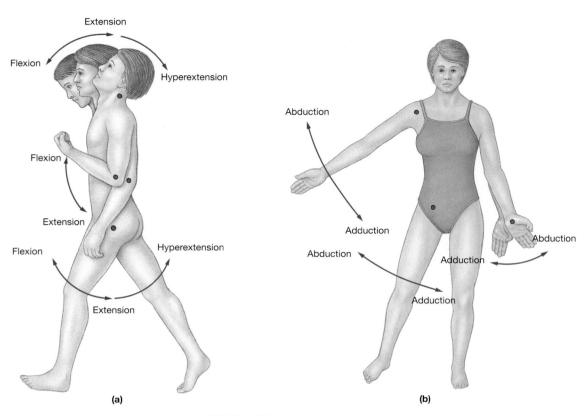

•**FIGURE 9-3** Angular Movements

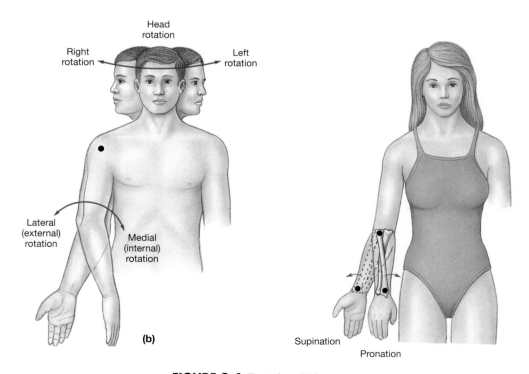

•**FIGURE 9-4** Rotational Movements

© 2002 Prentice Hall, Inc.

NOTES

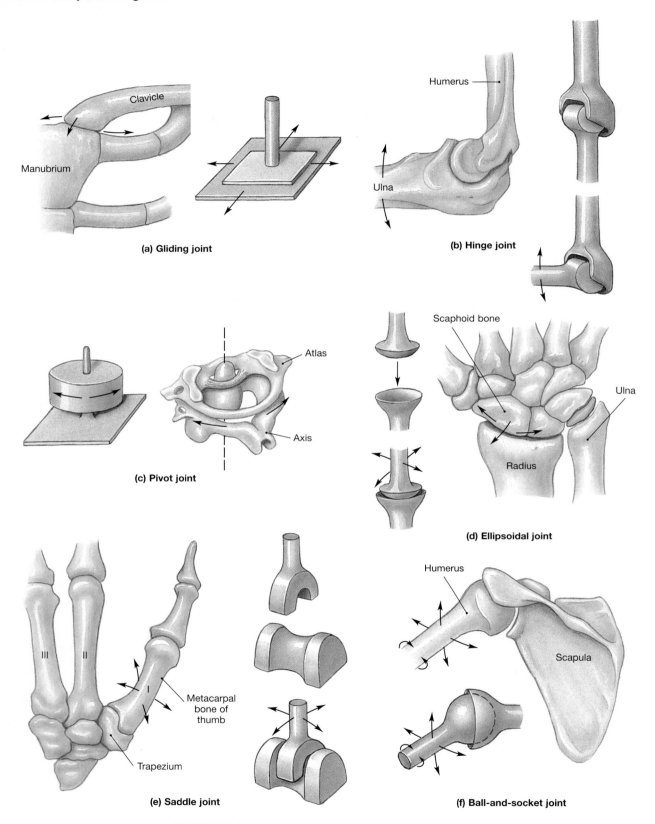

•**FIGURE 9-6** A Functional Classification of Synovial Joints

NOTES

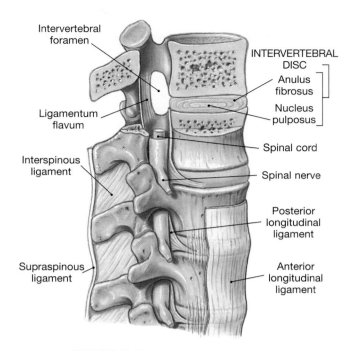

•FIGURE 9-7 **Intervertebral Articulations**

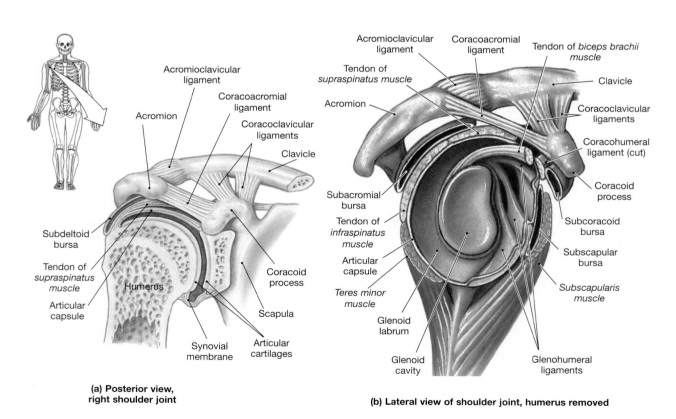

(a) Posterior view,
right shoulder joint

(b) Lateral view of shoulder joint, humerus removed

•FIGURE 9-9 **The Shoulder Joint**

NOTES

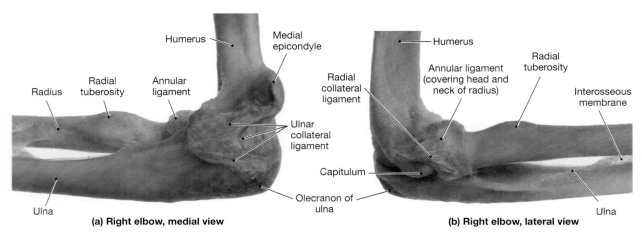

Humerus

Medial epicondyle

Radius

Radial tuberosity

Annular ligament

Radial collateral ligament

Ulnar collateral ligament

Ulna

(a) Right elbow, medial view

Humerus

Annular ligament (covering head and neck of radius)

Radial tuberosity

Interosseous membrane

Capitulum

Olecranon of ulna

Ulna

(b) Right elbow, lateral view

•FIGURE 9-10 The Elbow Joint

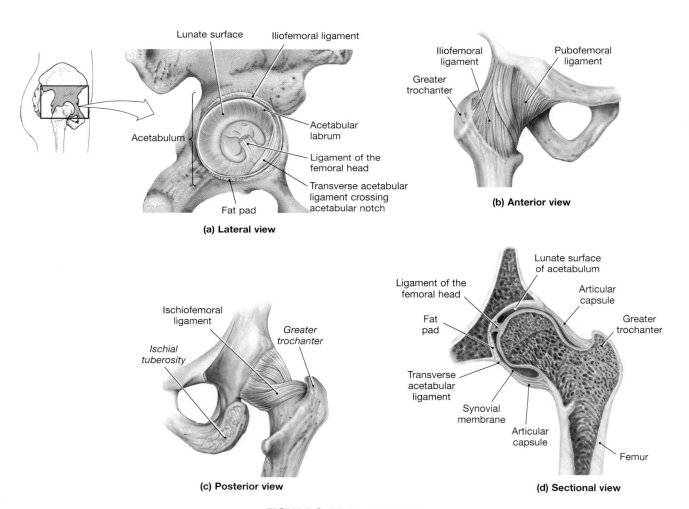

Lunate surface

Iliofemoral ligament

Acetabulum

Acetabular labrum

Ligament of the femoral head

Transverse acetabular ligament crossing acetabular notch

Fat pad

(a) Lateral view

Iliofemoral ligament

Pubofemoral ligament

Greater trochanter

(b) Anterior view

Ischiofemoral ligament

Ischial tuberosity

Greater trochanter

(c) Posterior view

Ligament of the femoral head

Lunate surface of acetabulum

Articular capsule

Fat pad

Greater trochanter

Transverse acetabular ligament

Synovial membrane

Articular capsule

Femur

(d) Sectional view

•FIGURE 9-11 The Hip Joint

NOTES

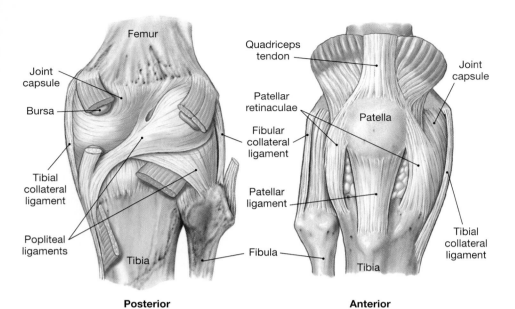

Posterior **Anterior**

(a) Superficial view, extended

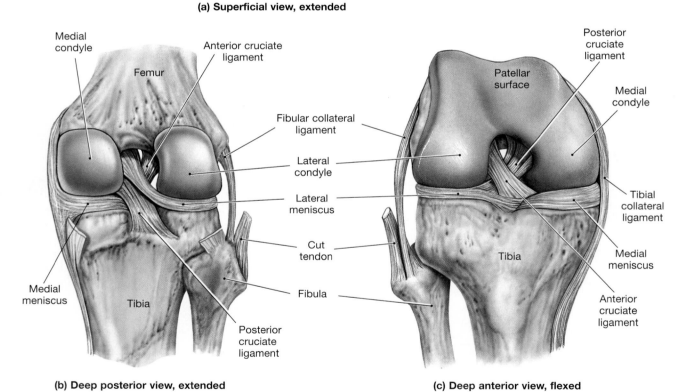

(b) Deep posterior view, extended **(c) Deep anterior view, flexed**

•**FIGURE 9-12** The Knee Joint

NOTES

10   Muscle Tissue

CHAPTER OUTLINE

INTRODUCTION
SKELETAL MUSCLE TISSUE AND THE MUSCULAR SYSTEM
ANATOMY OF SKELETAL MUSCLE
ORGANIZATION OF CONNECTIVE TISSUES
BLOOD VESSELS AND NERVES
MICROANATOMY OF SKELETAL MUSCLE FIBERS
CONTRACTION OF SKELETAL MUSCLE
THE SLIDING FILAMENT THEORY
THE CONTROL OF SKELETAL MUSCLE ACTIVITY
RELAXATION
LENGTH–TENSION RELATIONSHIPS
MUSCLE MECHANICS
TENSION PRODUCTION
ENERGETICS OF MUSCULAR ACTIVITY
MUSCLE PERFORMANCE
AGING AND THE MUSCULAR SYSTEM
INTEGRATION WITH OTHER SYSTEMS
CARDIAC MUSCLE TISSUE
DIFFERENCES BETWEEN CARDIAC AND SKELETAL MUSCLE TISSUES
SMOOTH MUSCLE TISSUE
DIFFERENCES BETWEEN SMOOTH MUSCLE TISSUE AND OTHER MUSCLE TISSUES

CHAPTER OBJECTIVES

1. Describe the characteristics and functions of skeletal muscle tissue.
2. Describe the organization of muscle at the tissue level.
3. Explain the unique characteristics of skeletal muscle fibers.
4. Identify the structural components of a sarcomere.
5. Identify the components of the neuromuscular junction and summarize the events involved in the neural control of skeletal muscles.
6. Explain the key steps involved in the contraction of a skeletal muscle fiber.
7. Compare the types of muscle contractions.
8. Describe the mechanisms by which muscle fibers obtain the energy to power contractions.
9. Relate the types of muscle fibers to muscle performance.
10. Distinguish between aerobic and anaerobic endurance, and explain their implications for muscular performance.
11. Describe the effects of aging on muscles.
12. Give examples of interactions between the muscular system and each of the other organ systems.
13. Identify the structural and functional differences among skeletal, cardiac, and smooth muscle cells.
14. Discuss the role that smooth muscle tissue plays in systems throughout the body.

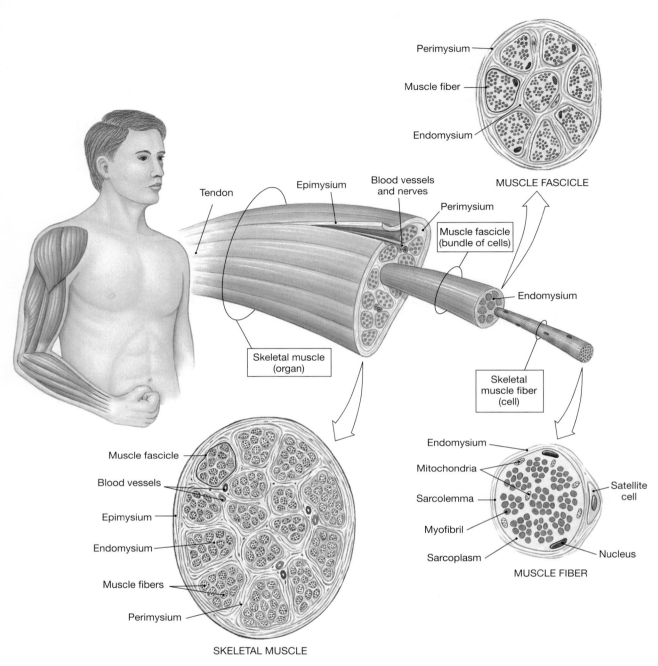

Perimysium

Muscle fiber

Endomysium

MUSCLE FASCICLE

Tendon

Epimysium

Blood vessels
and nerves

Perimysium

Muscle fascicle
(bundle of cells)

Endomysium

Skeletal muscle
(organ)

Skeletal
muscle fiber
(cell)

Muscle fascicle

Blood vessels

Epimysium

Endomysium

Muscle fibers

Perimysium

SKELETAL MUSCLE

Endomysium

Mitochondria

Sarcolemma

Myofibril

Sarcoplasm

Satellite
cell

Nucleus

MUSCLE FIBER

•FIGURE 10-1 The Organization of Skeletal Muscles

NOTES

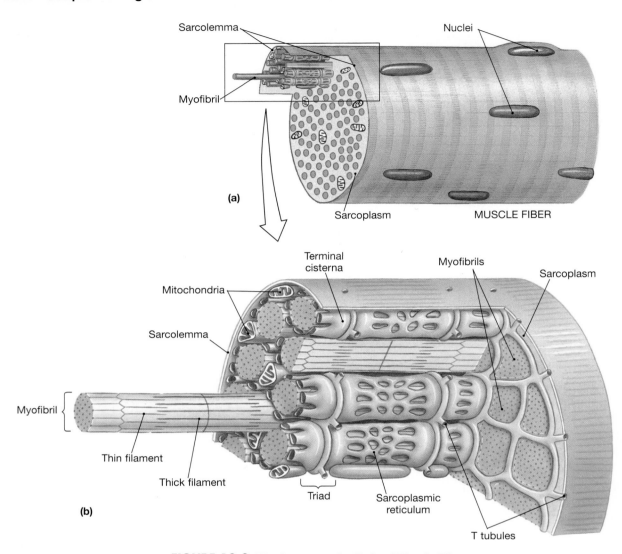

•**FIGURE 10-3** **The Structure of a Skeletal Muscle Fiber**

NOTES

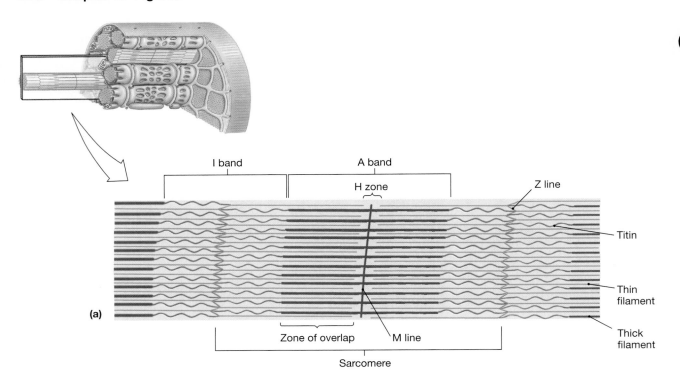

(a)

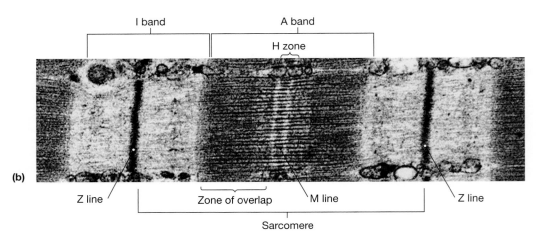

(b)

•**FIGURE 10-4** Sarcomere Structure, Part I

NOTES

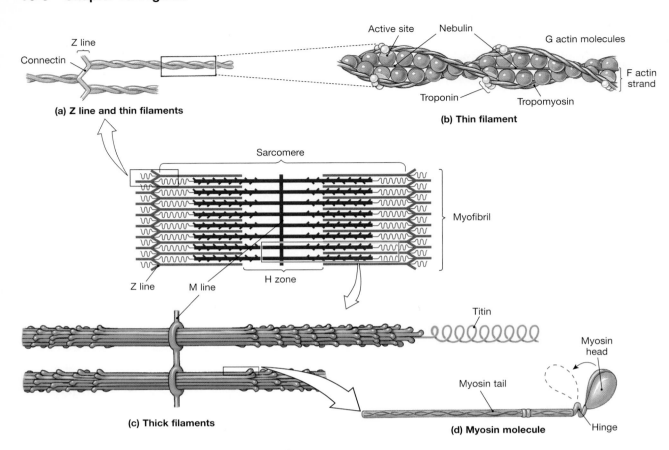

(a) Z line and thin filaments

Active site   Nebulin   G actin molecules

F actin strand

Troponin   Tropomyosin

(b) Thin filament

Sarcomere

Myofibril

Z line   M line   H zone

Titin

Myosin head

Myosin tail

(c) Thick filaments   (d) Myosin molecule   Hinge

Connectin

Z line

•FIGURE 10-7 Thick and Thin Filaments

NOTES

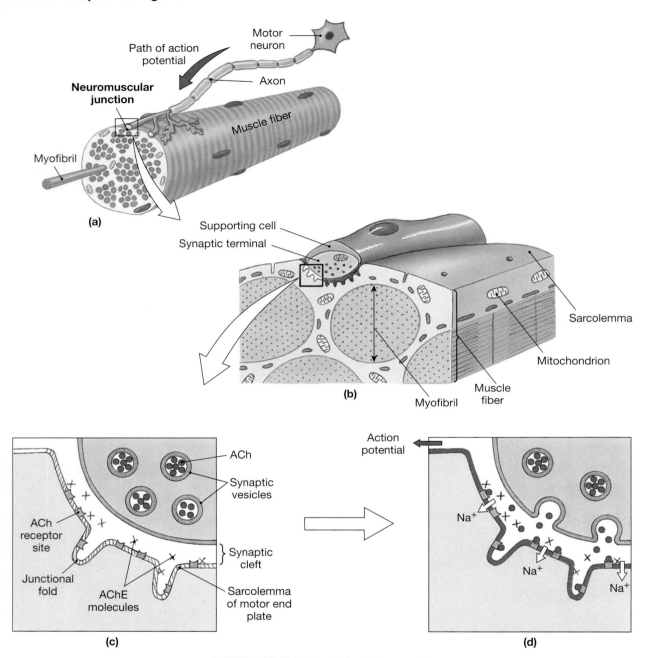

•**FIGURE 10-9** Skeletal Muscle Innervation

NOTES

•FIGURE 10-10 The Molecular Events of the Contraction Process

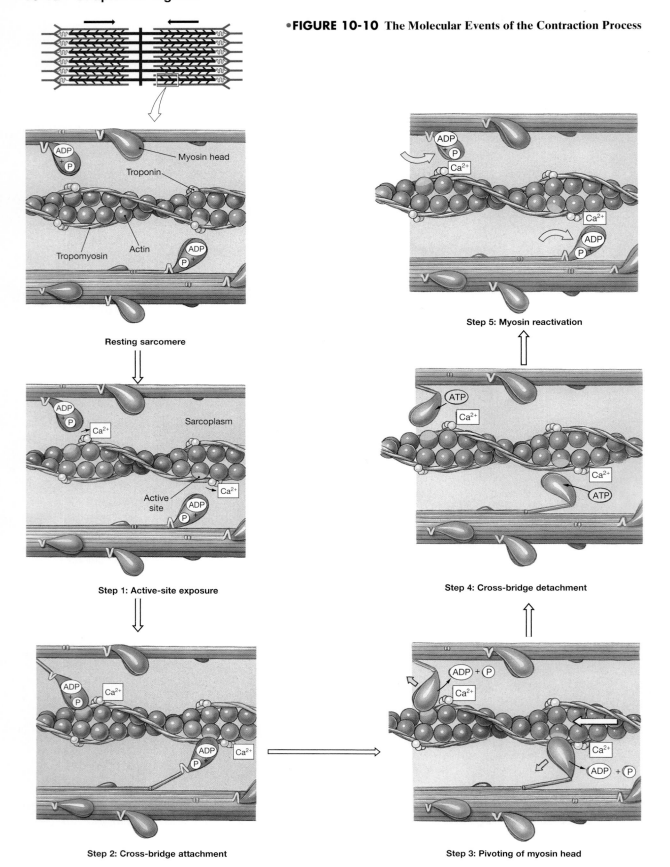

Resting sarcomere

Step 1: Active-site exposure

Step 2: Cross-bridge attachment

Step 3: Pivoting of myosin head

Step 4: Cross-bridge detachment

Step 5: Myosin reactivation

NOTES

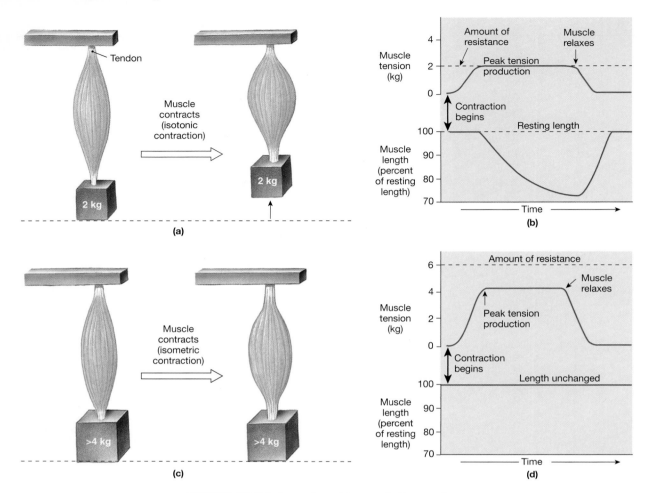

•FIGURE 10-16 Isotonic and Isometric Contractions

NOTES

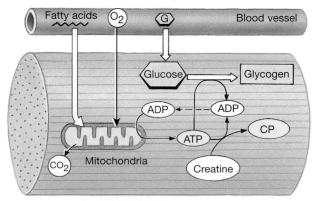

(a) Resting muscle: Fatty acids are catabolized; the ATP produced is used to build energy reserves of ATP, CP, and glycogen.

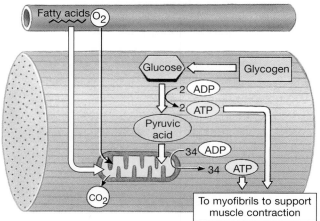

(b) Moderate activity: Glucose and fatty acids are catabolized; the ATP produced is used to power contraction.

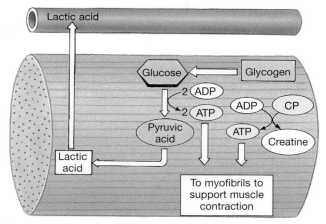

(c) Peak activity: Most ATP is produced through glycolysis, with lactic acid as a byproduct. Mitochondrial activity (not shown) now provides only about one-third of the ATP consumed.

•**FIGURE 10-18** Muscle Metabolism

NOTES

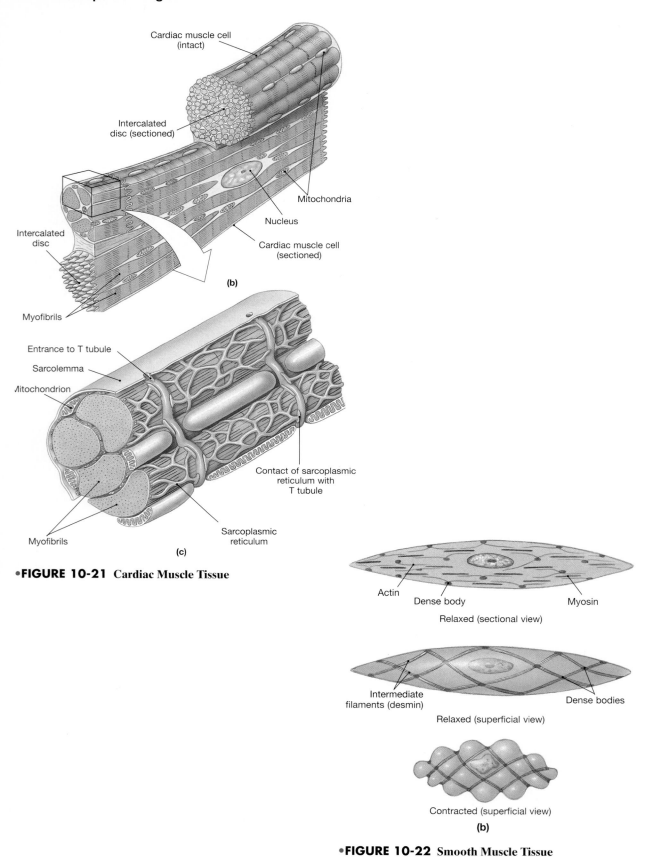

•**FIGURE 10-21** Cardiac Muscle Tissue

•**FIGURE 10-22** Smooth Muscle Tissue

NOTES

11 The Muscular System

CHAPTER OUTLINE

CHAPTER OBJECTIVES

1. Describe the arrangement of fascicles in the various types of muscles, and explain the resulting functional differences.
2. Describe the classes of levers and how they make muscles more efficient.
3. Predict the actions of a muscle on the basis of the relative positions of its origin and insertion.
4. Explain how muscles interact to produce or oppose movements.
5. Explain how the name of a muscle can help identify its location, appearance, and/or function.
6. Identify the principal axial muscles of the body together with their origins, insertions, actions, and innervation.
7. Identify the principal appendicular muscles of the body together with their origins, insertions, actions, and innervation.
8. Compare the major muscle groups of the upper and lower limbs, and relate their differences to their functional roles.

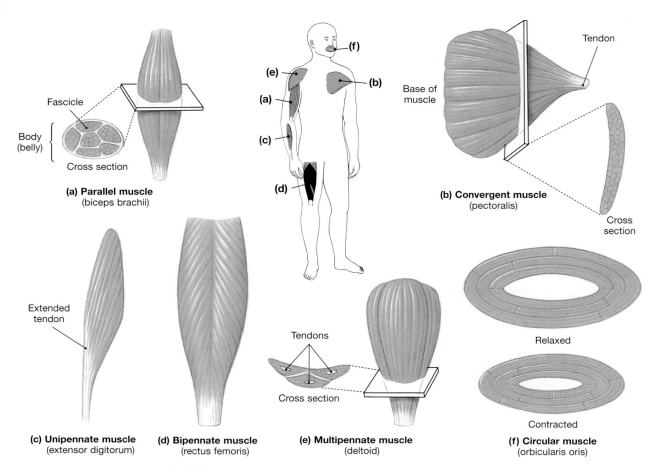

(a) Parallel muscle
(biceps brachii)

(b) Convergent muscle
(pectoralis)

(c) Unipennate muscle
(extensor digitorum)

(d) Bipennate muscle
(rectus femoris)

(e) Multipennate muscle
(deltoid)

(f) Circular muscle
(orbicularis oris)

•**FIGURE 11-1** Different Arrangements of Skeletal Muscle Fibers

NOTES

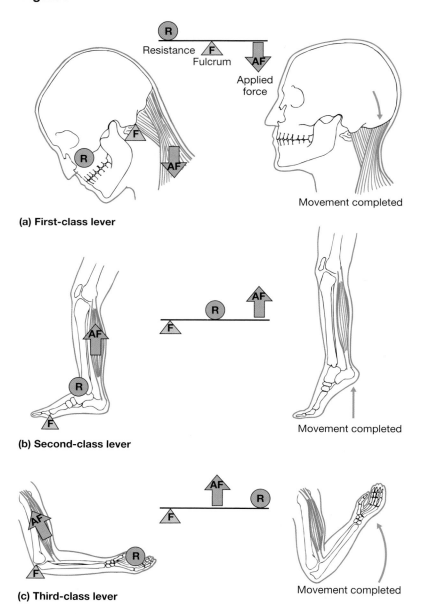

(a) First-class lever

(b) Second-class lever

(c) Third-class lever

Resistance

Fulcrum

Applied force

Movement completed

•FIGURE 11-2 The Three Classes of Levers

NOTES

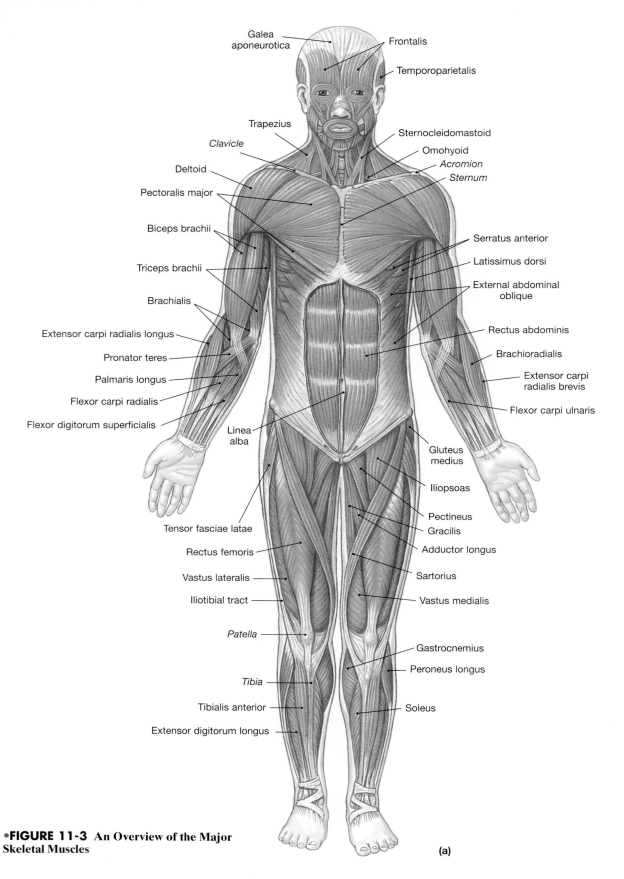

•**FIGURE 11-3** An Overview of the Major
Skeletal Muscles

(a)

NOTES

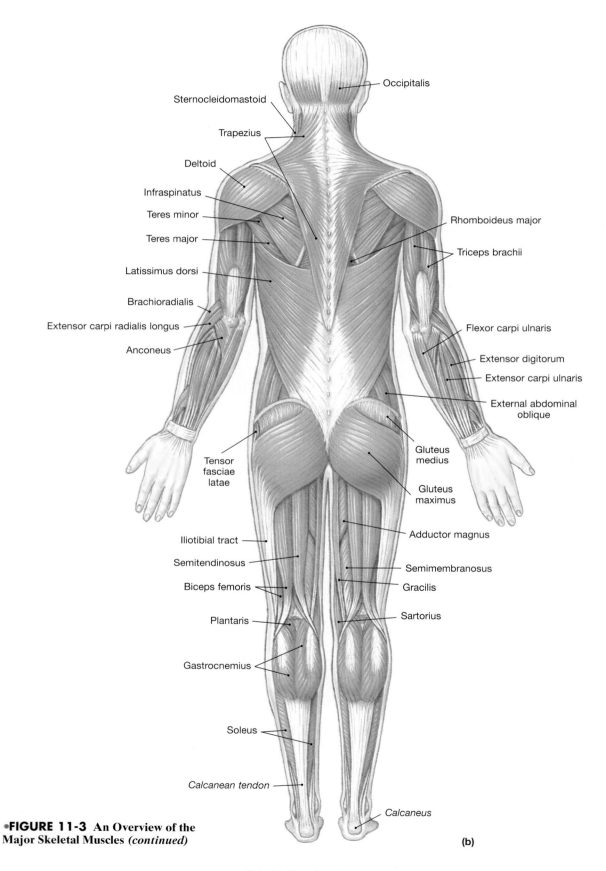

Occipitalis

Sternocleidomastoid

Trapezius

Deltoid

Infraspinatus

Teres minor

Teres major

Latissimus dorsi

Brachioradialis

Extensor carpi radialis longus

Anconeus

Rhomboideus major

Triceps brachii

Flexor carpi ulnaris

Extensor digitorum

Extensor carpi ulnaris

External abdominal
oblique

Gluteus
medius

Gluteus
maximus

Adductor magnus

Semimembranosus

Gracilis

Sartorius

Tensor
fasciae
latae

Iliotibial tract

Semitendinosus

Biceps femoris

Plantaris

Gastrocnemius

Soleus

Calcanean tendon

Calcaneus

•FIGURE 11-3 An Overview of the
Major Skeletal Muscles (continued)

(b)

NOTES

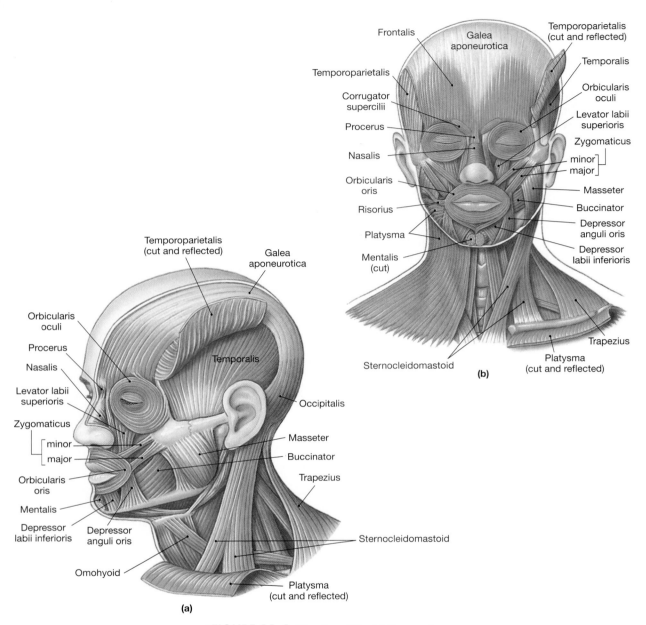

•**FIGURE 11-4** Muscles of Facial Expression

NOTES

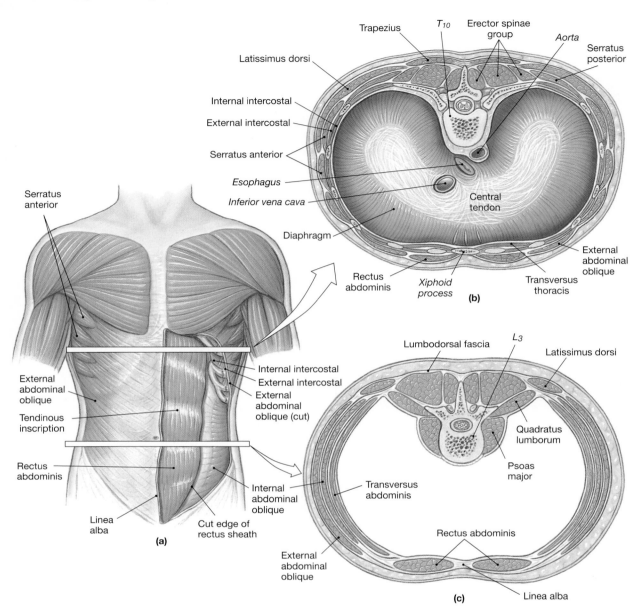

•**FIGURE 11-12** Oblique and Rectus Muscles and the Diaphragm

NOTES

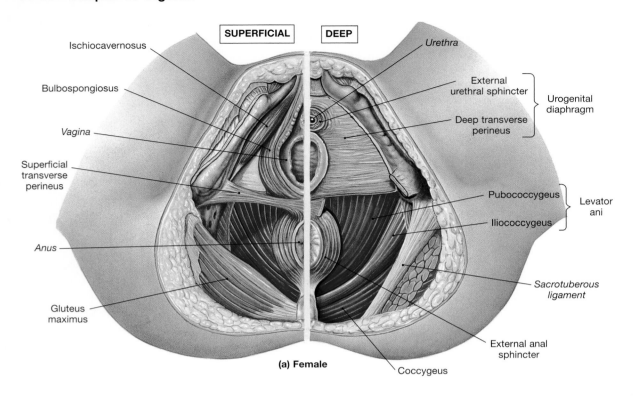

Ischiocavernosus

Bulbospongiosus

Vagina

Superficial
transverse
perineus

Anus

Gluteus
maximus

SUPERFICIAL   DEEP

Urethra

External
urethral sphincter

Deep transverse
perineus

Urogenital
diaphragm

Pubococcygeus

Iliococcygeus

Levator
ani

*Sacrotuberous
ligament*

External anal
sphincter

Coccygeus

(a) Female

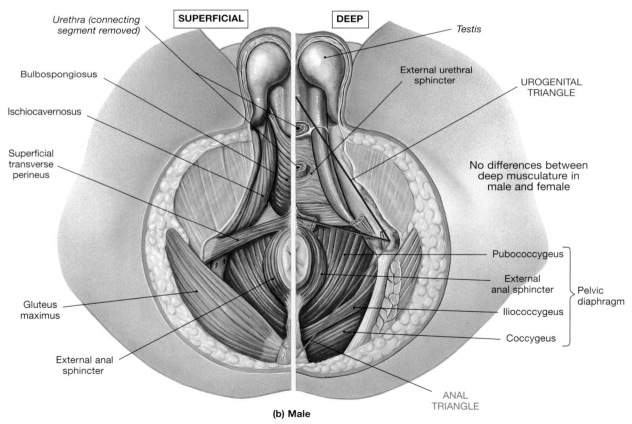

*Urethra (connecting
segment removed)*

Bulbospongiosus

Ischiocavernosus

Superficial
transverse
perineus

Gluteus
maximus

External anal
sphincter

SUPERFICIAL   DEEP

Testis

External urethral
sphincter

UROGENITAL
TRIANGLE

No differences between
deep musculature in
male and female

Pubococcygeus

External
anal sphincter

Iliococcygeus

Coccygeus

Pelvic
diaphragm

ANAL
TRIANGLE

(b) Male

•**FIGURE 11-13** Muscles of the Pelvic Floor

NOTES

12 Neural Tissue

CHAPTER OUTLINE

CHAPTER OBJECTIVES

1. List the two major anatomical divisions of the nervous system, and describe the characteristics of each division.
2. Sketch and label the structure of a typical neuron, and describe the functions of each component.
3. Classify neurons on the basis of their structure and function.
4. Describe the locations and functions of neuroglia.
5. Explain how the resting potential is created and maintained.
6. Describe the events involved in the generation and propagation of an action potential.
7. Discuss the factors that affect the speed with which action potentials are propagated.
8. Describe the structure of a synapse, and explain the mechanism involved in synaptic activity.
9. Describe the major types of neurotransmitters and neuromodulators, and discuss their effects on postsynaptic membranes.
10. Discuss the interactions that make possible the processing of information in neural tissue.
11. Describe the patterns of interaction between neurons that are involved in the processing of information at higher levels.
12. Give examples of interactions between the nervous system and each of the other organ systems.

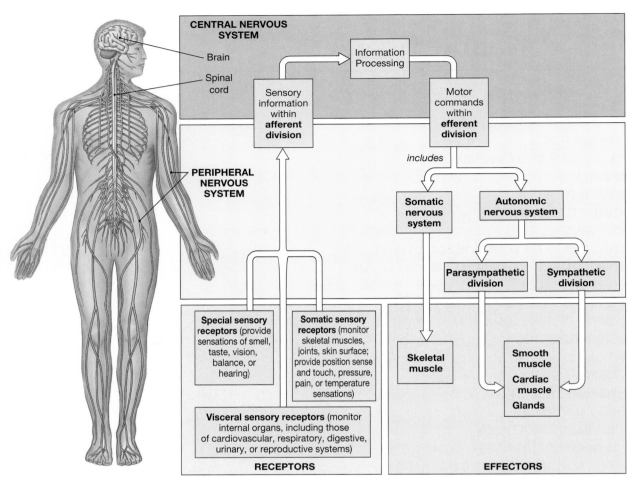

•**FIGURE 12-1** A Functional Overview of the Nervous System

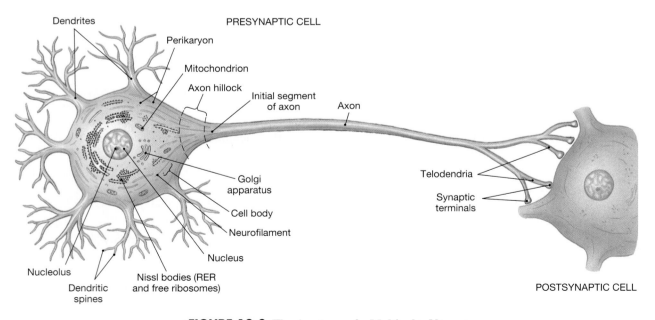

•**FIGURE 12-2** The Anatomy of a Multipolar Neuron

NOTES

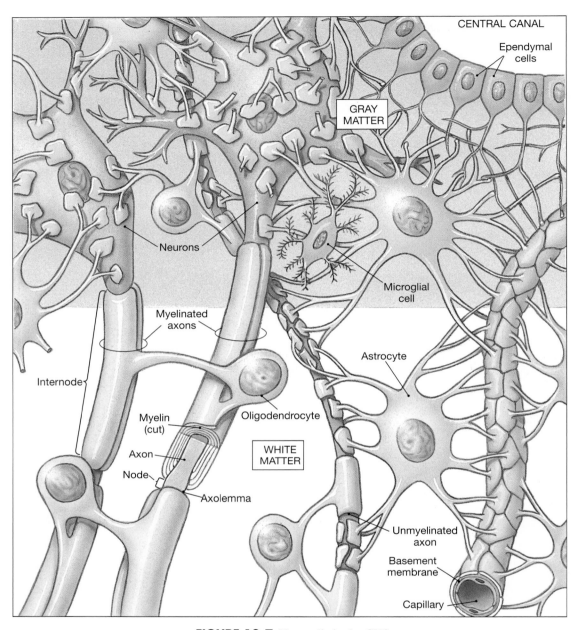

•FIGURE 12-7 Neuroglia in the CNS

NOTES

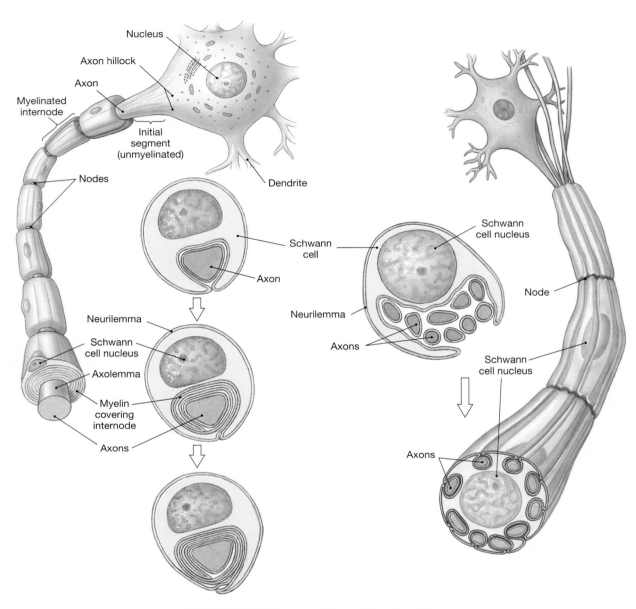

Nucleus

Axon hillock

Axon

Myelinated internode

Initial segment (unmyelinated)

Nodes

Dendrite

Schwann cell

Axon

Neurilemma

Schwann cell nucleus

Axolemma

Myelin covering internode

Axons

Schwann cell nucleus

Neurilemma

Axons

Node

Schwann cell nucleus

Axons

•**FIGURE 12-8** Schwann Cells and Peripheral Axons

NOTES

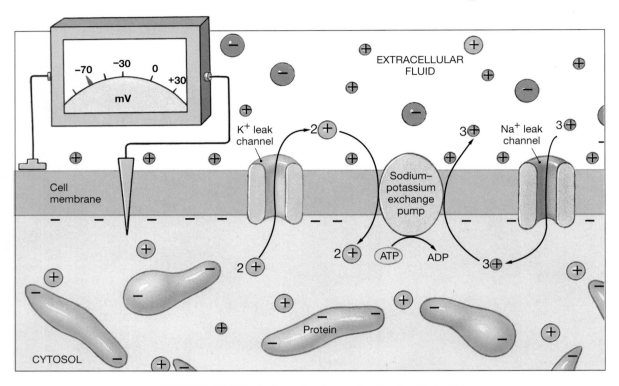

•**FIGURE 12-11** **An Introduction to the Resting Potential**

NOTES

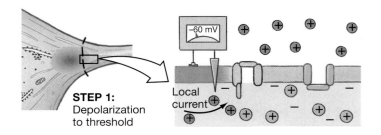

STEP 1:
Depolarization
to threshold

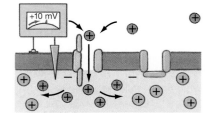

STEP 2:
Activation of sodium
channels and rapid
depolarization

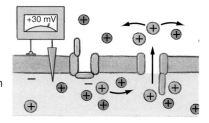

STEP 3:
Inactivation of sodium
channels and activation
of potassium channels

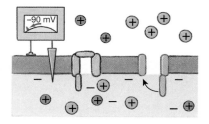

STEP 4:
The return to
normal permeability

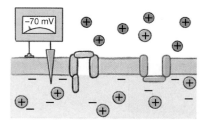

STEP 5:
Resting state

•**FIGURE 12-15** The Generation of an Action Potential

NOTES

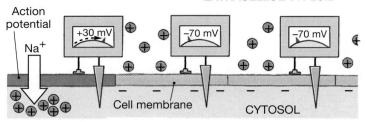

(a) As an action potential develops in the initial segment, the transmembrane potential depolarizes to +30 mV.

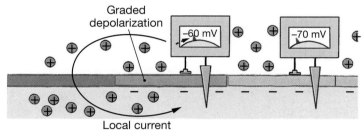

(b) A local current depolarizes the adjacent portion of the membrane to threshold.

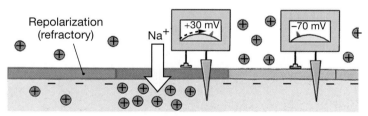

(c) An action potential develops at this location, and the initial segment enters the refractory period.

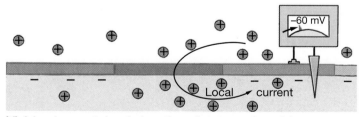

(d) A local current depolarizes the adjacent portion of the membrane to threshold, and the cycle is repeated.

•FIGURE 12-16 Action Potential Propagation along an Unmyelinated Axon

NOTES

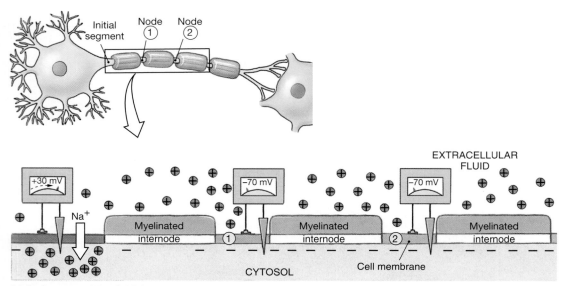

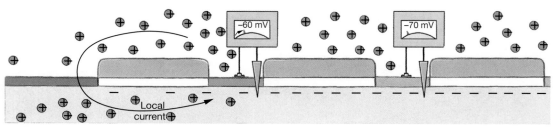

(a) Action potential at initial segment

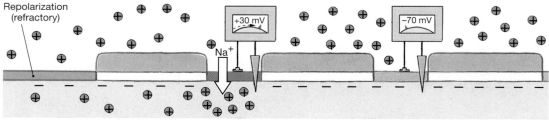

(b) Depolarization to threshold at node 1

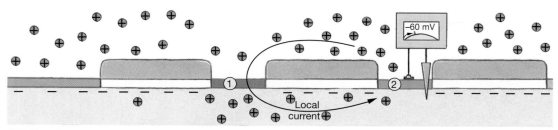

(c) Action potential at node 1

(d) Depolarization to threshold at node 2

•**FIGURE 12-17** Saltatory Propagation along a Myelinated Axon

NOTES

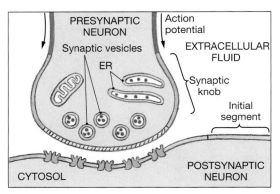

(a) STEP 1: Arrival of action potential at synaptic knob

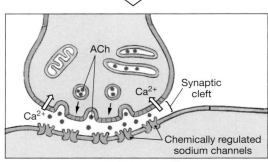

(b) STEP 2: Entry of extracellular Ca^{2+} and exocytosis of ACh

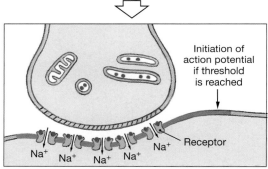

(c) STEP 3: Binding of ACh to receptors and depolarization of postsynaptic membrane may bring initial segment to threshold

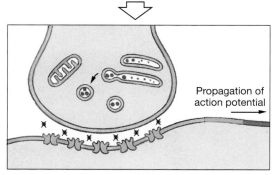

(d) STEP 4: Removal of ACh by acetylcholinesterase (AChE)

•**FIGURE 12-18** The Function of a Cholinergic Synapse

NOTES

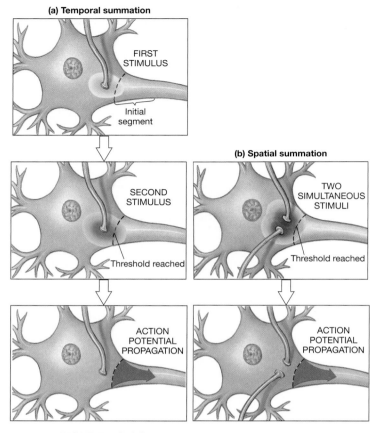

(a) Temporal summation

(b) Spatial summation

•FIGURE 12-20 Temporal and Spatial Summation

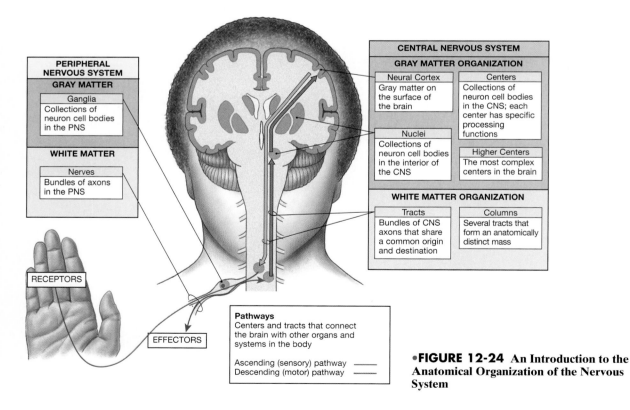

•FIGURE 12-24 An Introduction to the Anatomical Organization of the Nervous System

NOTES

13   The Spinal Cord and Spinal Nerves

CHAPTER OUTLINE

CHAPTER OBJECTIVES

1. Discuss the structure and functions of the spinal cord.
2. Describe the three meningeal layers that surround the central nervous system.
3. Explain the roles of white matter and gray matter in processing and relaying sensory information and motor commands.
4. Describe the major components of a spinal nerve.
5. Relate the distribution pattern of spinal nerves to the regions they innervate.
6. Describe the process of a neural reflex.
7. Classify the types of reflexes, and explain the functions of each.
8. Distinguish between the types of motor responses produced by various reflexes.
9. Explain how reflexes interact to produce complex behaviors.
10. Explain how higher centers control and modify reflex responses.

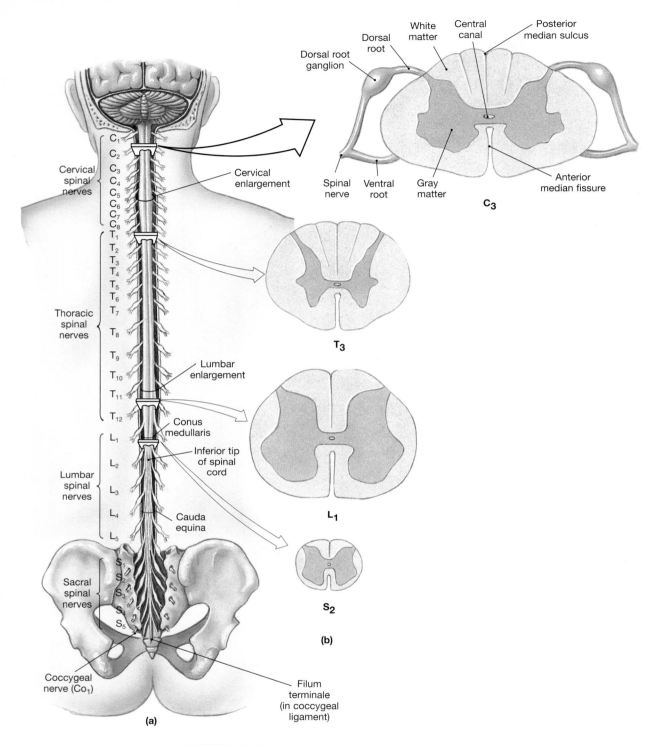

•FIGURE 13-1 Gross Anatomy of the Adult Spinal Cord

NOTES

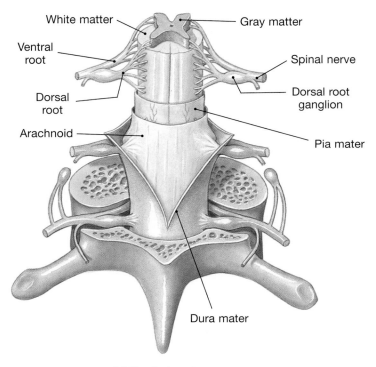

White matter

Gray matter

Ventral
root

Spinal nerve

Dorsal
root

Dorsal root
ganglion

Arachnoid

Pia mater

Dura mater

(a) Posterior view

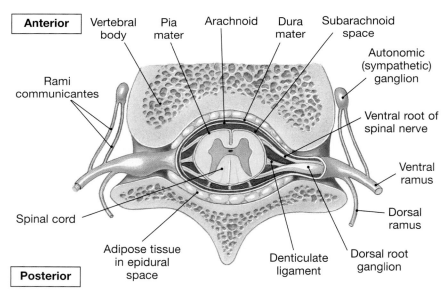

| Anterior | Vertebral
body | Pia
mater | Arachnoid | Dura
mater | Subarachnoid
space |

Autonomic
(sympathetic)
ganglion

Rami
communicantes

Ventral root of
spinal nerve

Ventral
ramus

Spinal cord

Dorsal
ramus

Adipose tissue
in epidural
space

Denticulate
ligament

Dorsal root
ganglion

Posterior

(b) Sectional view

•**FIGURE 13-2** The Spinal Cord and Spinal Meninges

NOTES

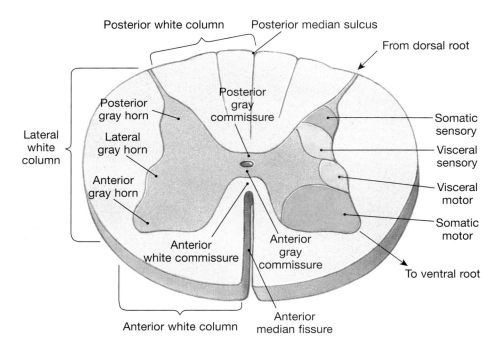

Posterior white column · Posterior median sulcus

From dorsal root

Posterior gray commissure

Posterior gray horn

Lateral gray horn

Anterior gray horn

Lateral white column

Somatic sensory

Visceral sensory

Visceral motor

Somatic motor

Anterior white commissure

Anterior gray commissure

To ventral root

Anterior white column

Anterior median fissure

•**FIGURE 13-5** **The Sectional Organization of the Spinal Cord**

NOTES

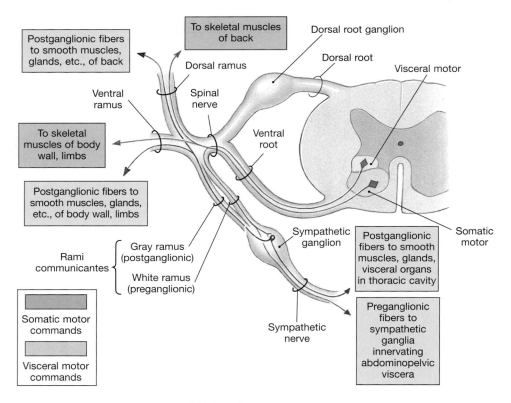

(a) Motor fibers

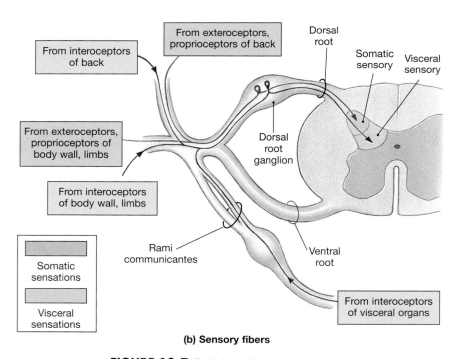

(b) Sensory fibers

•**FIGURE 13-7** Peripheral Distribution of Spinal Nerves

NOTES

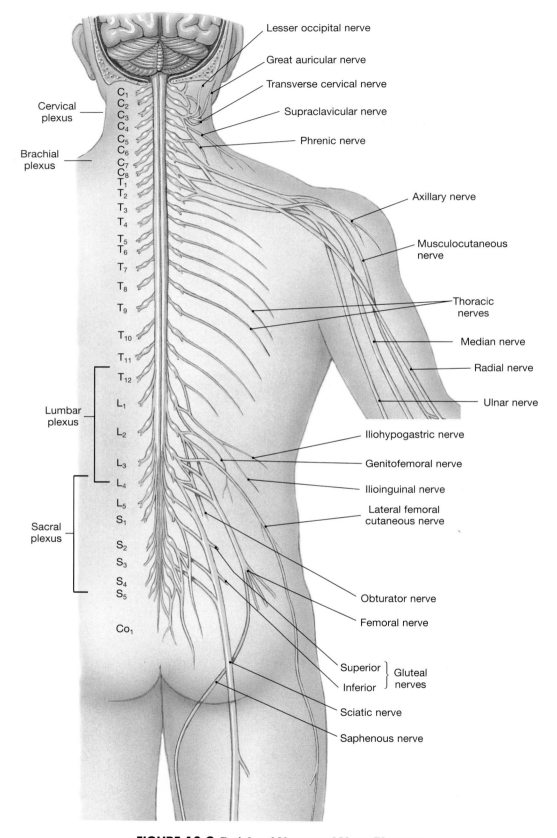

•**FIGURE 13-9** Peripheral Nerves and Nerve Plexuses

NOTES

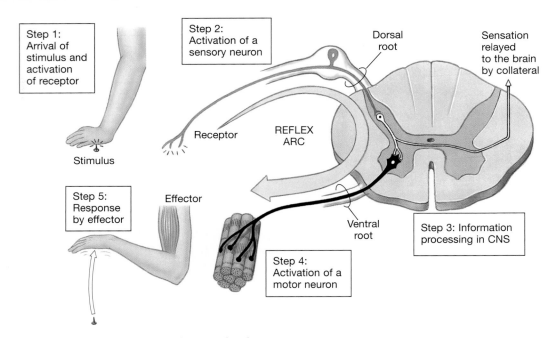

Step 1:
Arrival of
stimulus and
activation
of receptor

Step 2:
Activation of a
sensory neuron

Dorsal
root

Sensation
relayed
to the brain
by collateral

Receptor

REFLEX
ARC

Stimulus

Step 5:
Response
by effector

Effector

Ventral
root

Step 3: Information
processing in CNS

Step 4:
Activation of a
motor neuron

•FIGURE 13-13 Components of a Reflex Arc

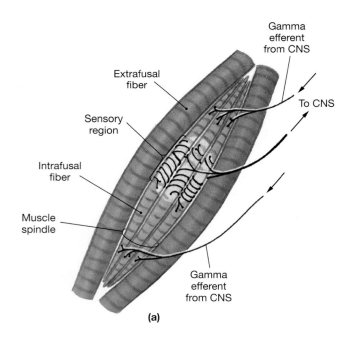

Gamma
efferent
from CNS

Extrafusal
fiber

To CNS

Sensory
region

Intrafusal
fiber

Muscle
spindle

Gamma
efferent
from CNS

(a)

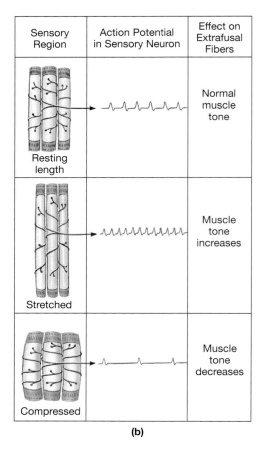

Sensory Region	Action Potential in Sensory Neuron	Effect on Extrafusal Fibers
Resting length		Normal muscle tone
Stretched		Muscle tone increases
Compressed		Muscle tone decreases

(b)

•FIGURE 13-18 Intrafusal Fibers

NOTES

CHAPTER

14   The Brain and Cranial Nerves

CHAPTER OUTLINE

CHAPTER OBJECTIVES

1. Name the major regions of the brain, and describe their functions.
2. Name the ventricles of the brain, and describe their locations and the connections between them.
3. Explain how the brain is protected and supported.
4. Discuss the formation, circulation, and functions of the cerebrospinal fluid.
5. Locate the motor, sensory, and association areas of the cerebral cortex, and discuss their functions.
6. Identify important structures within each region of the brain, and explain their functions.
7. Identify the cranial nerves, and relate each nerve to its principal destinations and functions.

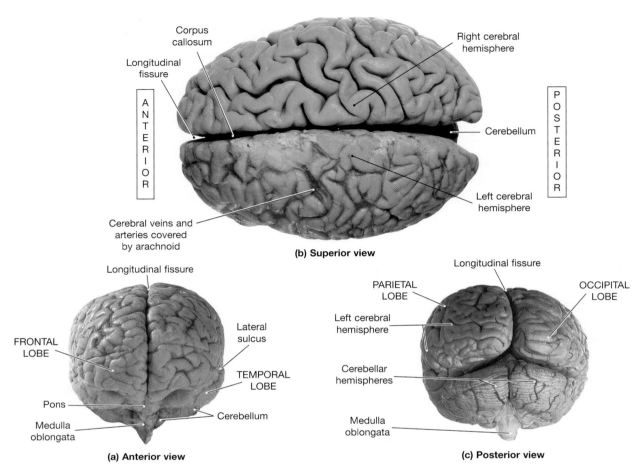

Corpus callosum

Longitudinal fissure

Right cerebral hemisphere

ANTERIOR

POSTERIOR

Cerebellum

Left cerebral hemisphere

Cerebral veins and arteries covered by arachnoid

(b) Superior view

Longitudinal fissure

FRONTAL LOBE

Lateral sulcus

TEMPORAL LOBE

Pons

Cerebellum

Medulla oblongata

(a) Anterior view

Longitudinal fissure

PARIETAL LOBE

OCCIPITAL LOBE

Left cerebral hemisphere

Cerebellar hemispheres

Medulla oblongata

(c) Posterior view

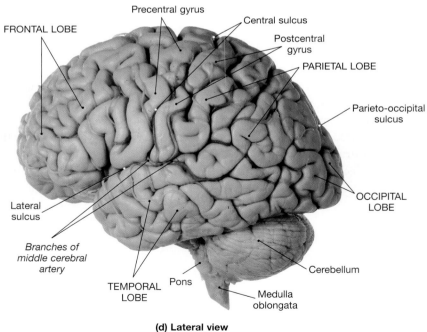

Precentral gyrus

Central sulcus

FRONTAL LOBE

Postcentral gyrus

PARIETAL LOBE

Parieto-occipital sulcus

OCCIPITAL LOBE

Lateral sulcus

Branches of middle cerebral artery

TEMPORAL LOBE

Pons

Cerebellum

Medulla oblongata

(d) Lateral view

•**FIGURE 14-1** The Adult Brain

NOTES

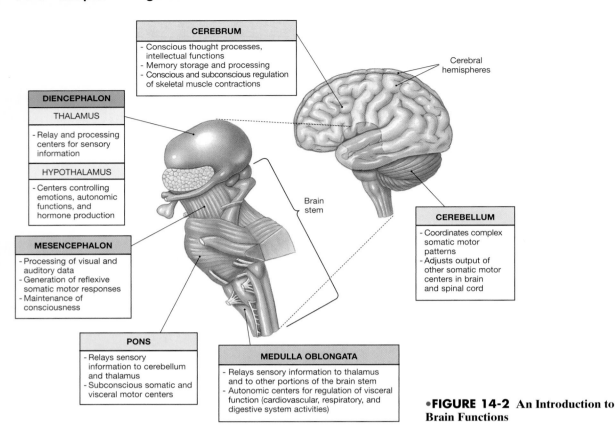

CEREBRUM
- Conscious thought processes, intellectual functions
- Memory storage and processing
- Conscious and subconscious regulation of skeletal muscle contractions

Cerebral hemispheres

DIENCEPHALON

THALAMUS
- Relay and processing centers for sensory information

HYPOTHALAMUS
- Centers controlling emotions, autonomic functions, and hormone production

MESENCEPHALON
- Processing of visual and auditory data
- Generation of reflexive somatic motor responses
- Maintenance of consciousness

Brain stem

CEREBELLUM
- Coordinates complex somatic motor patterns
- Adjusts output of other somatic motor centers in brain and spinal cord

PONS
- Relays sensory information to cerebellum and thalamus
- Subconscious somatic and visceral motor centers

MEDULLA OBLONGATA
- Relays sensory information to thalamus and to other portions of the brain stem
- Autonomic centers for regulation of visceral function (cardiovascular, respiratory, and digestive system activities)

•**FIGURE 14-2** An Introduction to Brain Functions

Dural sinus   Dura mater (endosteal layer)   Cranium (skull)
Dura mater (meningeal layer)
Subdural space
Arachnoid
Subarachnoid space
Pia mater
Cerebral cortex

Cerebral cortex

Cerebellum
Medulla oblongata
Spinal cord

(a)

Dura mater   Falx cerebri   Inferior sagittal sinus   Cranium
Superior sagittal sinus
Tentorium cerebelli
Transverse sinus
Falx cerebelli

(b)

•**FIGURE 14-4** The Relationship among the Brain, Cranium, and Meninges

NOTES

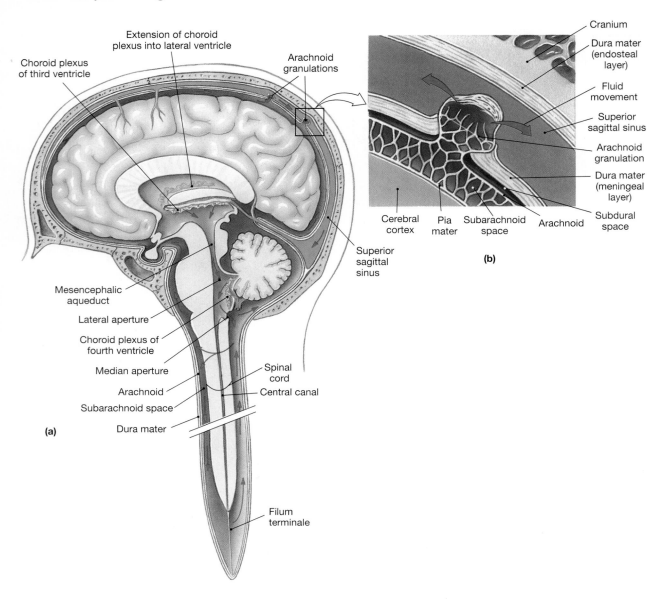

Extension of choroid
plexus into lateral ventricle

Choroid plexus
of third ventricle

Arachnoid
granulations

Mesencephalic
aqueduct

Lateral aperture

Choroid plexus of
fourth ventricle

Median aperture

Arachnoid

Subarachnoid space

Dura mater

Spinal
cord

Central canal

Superior
sagittal
sinus

Filum
terminale

(a)

Cranium

Dura mater
(endosteal
layer)

Fluid
movement

Superior
sagittal sinus

Arachnoid
granulation

Dura mater
(meningeal
layer)

Subdural
space

Cerebral
cortex

Pia
mater

Subarachnoid
space

Arachnoid

(b)

•**FIGURE 14-5** **The Circulation of Cerebrospinal Fluid**

NOTES

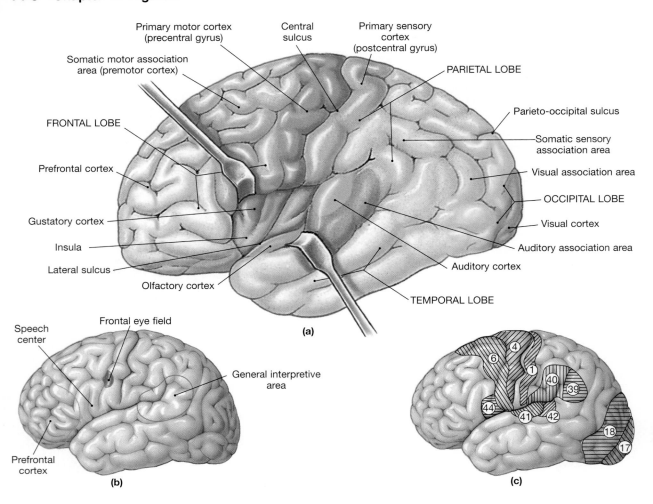

Primary motor cortex
(precentral gyrus)

Central
sulcus

Primary sensory
cortex
(postcentral gyrus)

Somatic motor association
area (premotor cortex)

PARIETAL LOBE

FRONTAL LOBE

Parieto-occipital sulcus

Prefrontal cortex

Somatic sensory
association area

Visual association area

Gustatory cortex

OCCIPITAL LOBE

Insula

Visual cortex

Lateral sulcus

Auditory association area

Olfactory cortex

Auditory cortex

TEMPORAL LOBE

(a)

Speech
center

Frontal eye field

General interpretive
area

Prefrontal
cortex

(b)

(c)

•FIGURE 14-8 The Cerebral Hemispheres

NOTES

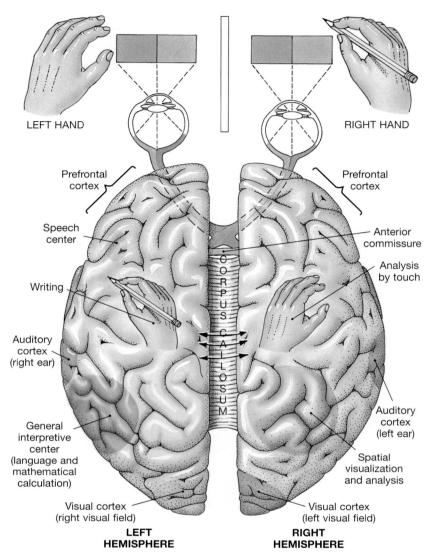

LEFT HAND

RIGHT HAND

Prefrontal cortex

Speech center

Writing

Auditory cortex (right ear)

General interpretive center (language and mathematical calculation)

Visual cortex (right visual field)

LEFT HEMISPHERE

CORPUS CALLOSUM

Prefrontal cortex

Anterior commissure

Analysis by touch

Auditory cortex (left ear)

Spatial visualization and analysis

Visual cortex (left visual field)

RIGHT HEMISPHERE

•**FIGURE 14-9** Hemispheric Lateralization

NOTES

15 Integrative Functions

CHAPTER OUTLINE

INTRODUCTION
SOMATIC SENSORY AND MOTOR PATHWAYS
SENSORY PATHWAYS
MOTOR PATHWAYS AND MOTOR CONTROL
MONITORING BRAIN ACTIVITY: THE ELECTROENCEPHALOGRAM
HIGHER-ORDER FUNCTIONS
MEMORY
CONSCIOUSNESS
BRAIN CHEMISTRY AND BEHAVIOR
PERSONALITY AND OTHER MYSTERIES
AGING AND THE NERVOUS SYSTEM
AGE-RELATED ANATOMICAL AND FUNCTIONAL CHANGES
ALZHEIMER'S DISEASE

CHAPTER OBJECTIVES

1. Identify the principal sensory and motor pathways.
2. Compare the components, processes, and functions of the various motor pathways.
3. Explain how we can distinguish among sensations that originate in different areas of the body.
4. Describe the levels of information processing involved in motor control.
5. Discuss how the brain integrates sensory information and coordinates responses.
6. Explain how memories are created, stored, and recalled.
7. Distinguish between the levels of consciousness and unconsciousness, and identify the characteristics of brain activity associated with the different levels of sleep.
8. Describe drug-related alterations in brain function.
9. Summarize the effects of aging on the nervous system.

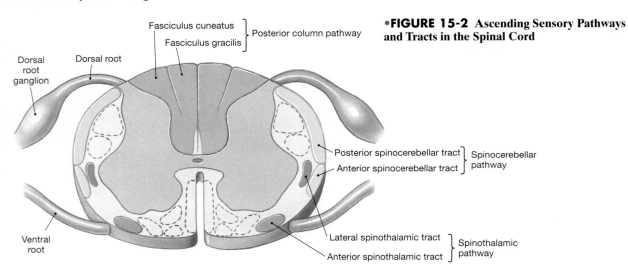

•**FIGURE 15-2** Ascending Sensory Pathways
and Tracts in the Spinal Cord

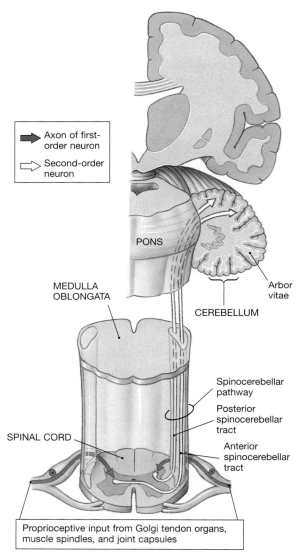

•**FIGURE 15-5** The Spinocerebellar Pathway

NOTES

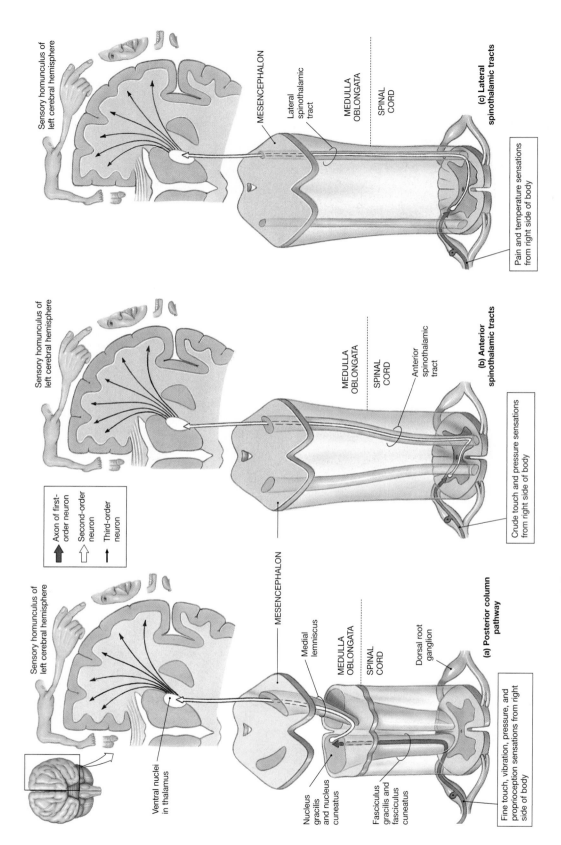

•FIGURE 15-3 The Posterior Column and Spinothalamic Pathways

NOTES

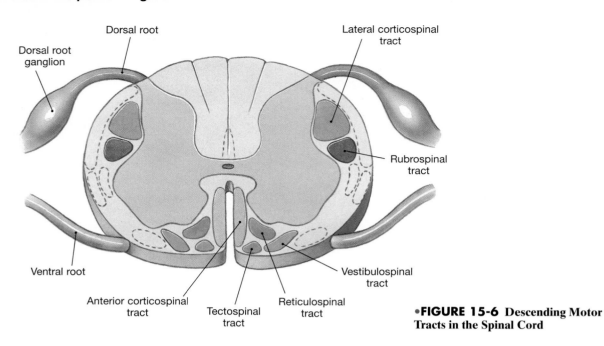

Dorsal root

Dorsal root
ganglion

Lateral corticospinal
tract

Rubrospinal
tract

Ventral root

Anterior corticospinal
tract

Tectospinal
tract

Reticulospinal
tract

Vestibulospinal
tract

•**FIGURE 15-6** Descending Motor
Tracts in the Spinal Cord

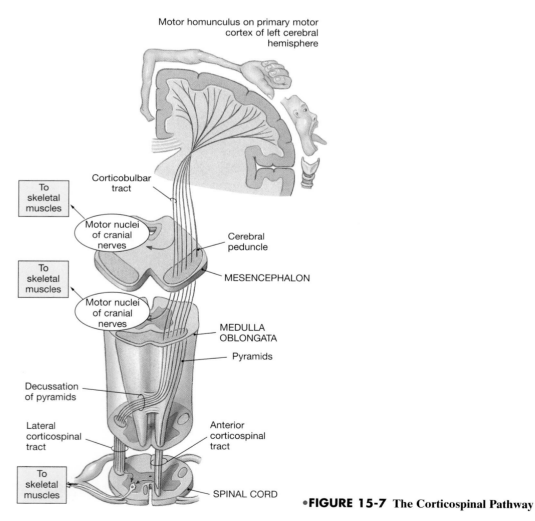

Motor homunculus on primary motor
cortex of left cerebral
hemisphere

Corticobulbar
tract

To
skeletal
muscles

Motor nuclei
of cranial
nerves

Cerebral
peduncle

MESENCEPHALON

To
skeletal
muscles

Motor nuclei
of cranial
nerves

MEDULLA
OBLONGATA

Pyramids

Decussation
of pyramids

Lateral
corticospinal
tract

Anterior
corticospinal
tract

To
skeletal
muscles

SPINAL CORD

•**FIGURE 15-7** The Corticospinal Pathway

NOTES

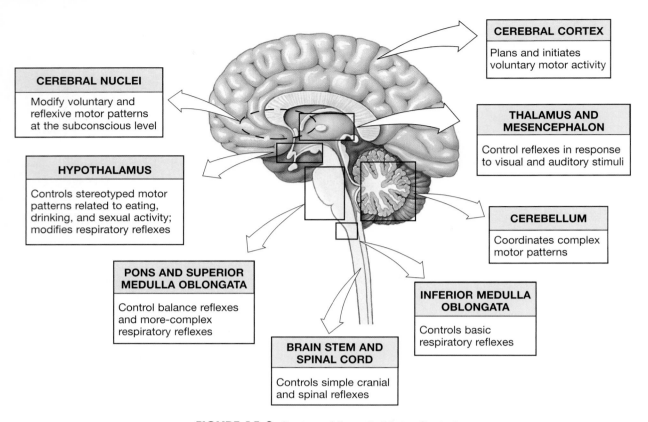

CEREBRAL CORTEX

Plans and initiates
voluntary motor activity

CEREBRAL NUCLEI

Modify voluntary and
reflexive motor patterns
at the subconscious level

**THALAMUS AND
MESENCEPHALON**

Control reflexes in response
to visual and auditory stimuli

HYPOTHALAMUS

Controls stereotyped motor
patterns related to eating,
drinking, and sexual activity;
modifies respiratory reflexes

CEREBELLUM

Coordinates complex
motor patterns

**PONS AND SUPERIOR
MEDULLA OBLONGATA**

Control balance reflexes
and more-complex
respiratory reflexes

**INFERIOR MEDULLA
OBLONGATA**

Controls basic
respiratory reflexes

**BRAIN STEM AND
SPINAL CORD**

Controls simple cranial
and spinal reflexes

•**FIGURE 15-8** Centers of Somatic Motor Control

NOTES

16 The Autonomic Nervous System

CHAPTER OUTLINE

CHAPTER OBJECTIVES

1. Compare the organization of the autonomic nervous system with that of the somatic nervous system.
2. Contrast the structures and functions of the sympathetic and parasympathetic divisions of the autonomic nervous system.
3. Describe the mechanisms of neurotransmitter release in the autonomic nervous system.
4. Compare the effects of the various autonomic neurotransmitters on target organs and tissues.
5. Discuss the relationship between the two divisions of the autonomic nervous system and the significance of dual innervation.
6. Explain the importance of autonomic tone.
7. Describe the hierarchy of interacting levels of control in the autonomic nervous system.

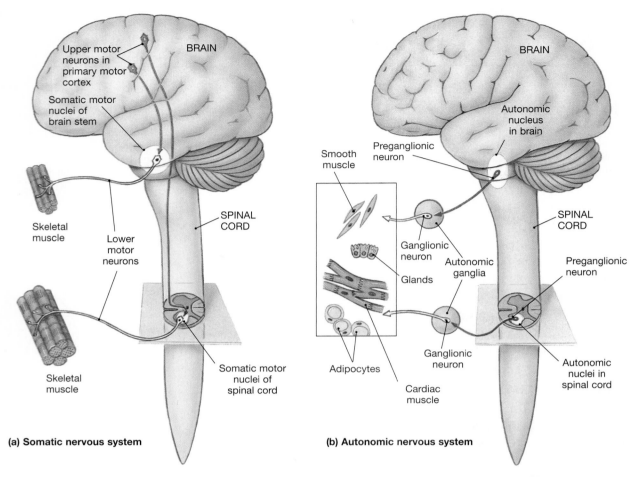

(a) Somatic nervous system   (b) Autonomic nervous system

•**FIGURE 16-1** The Organization of the Somatic and Autonomic Nervous Systems

NOTES

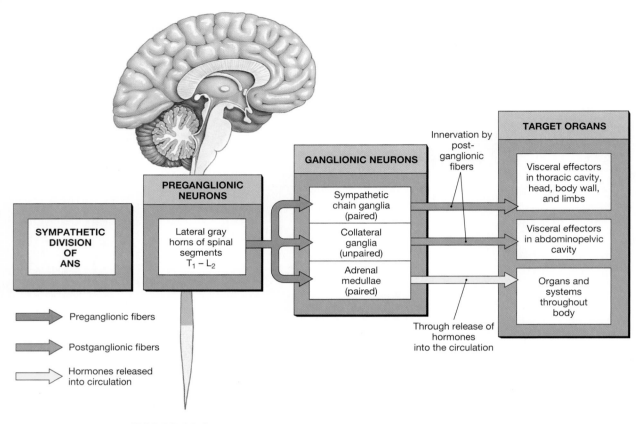

•**FIGURE 16-3** The Organization of the Sympathetic Division of the ANS

NOTES

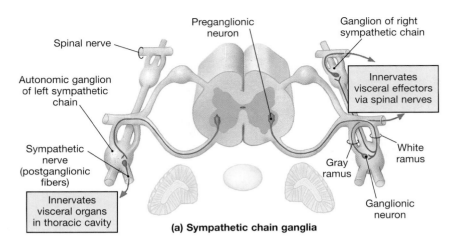

Preganglionic neuron

Spinal nerve

Autonomic ganglion of left sympathetic chain

Sympathetic nerve (postganglionic fibers)

Ganglion of right sympathetic chain

Innervates visceral effectors via spinal nerves

White ramus

Gray ramus

Ganglionic neuron

Innervates visceral organs in thoracic cavity

(a) Sympathetic chain ganglia

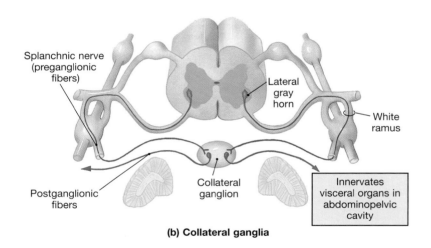

Splanchnic nerve (preganglionic fibers)

Lateral gray horn

White ramus

Postganglionic fibers

Collateral ganglion

Innervates visceral organs in abdominopelvic cavity

(b) Collateral ganglia

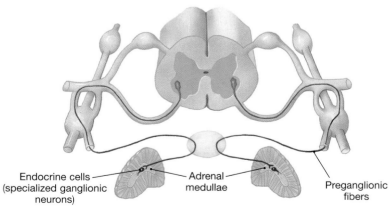

Endocrine cells (specialized ganglionic neurons)

Adrenal medullae

Preganglionic fibers

(c) The adrenal medullae

•**FIGURE 16-4** Sympathetic Pathways

NOTES

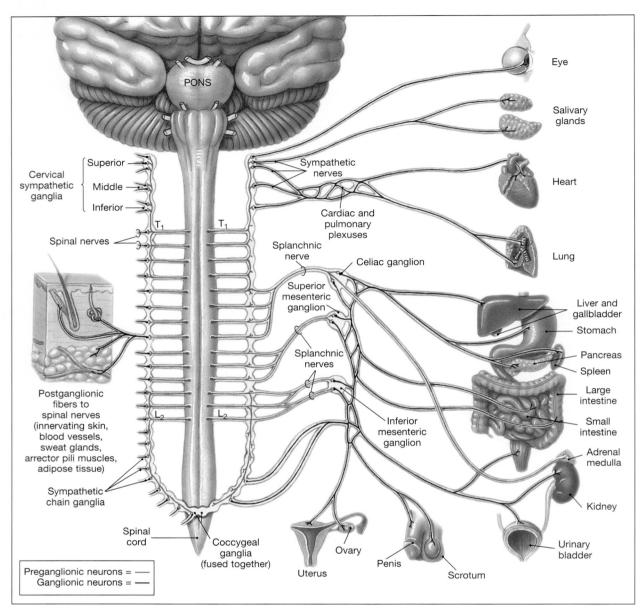

•**FIGURE 16-5** The Distribution of Sympathetic Innervation

NOTES

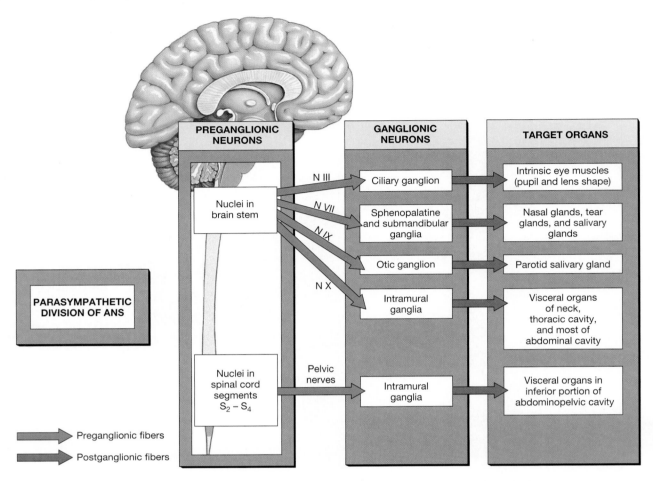

•**FIGURE 16-7** The Organization of the Parasympathetic Division of the ANS

NOTES

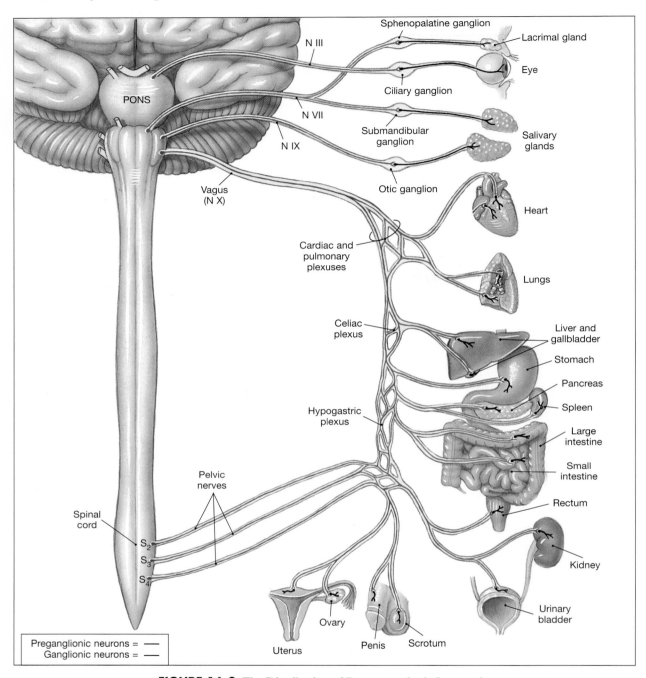

•**FIGURE 16-8** The Distribution of Parasympathetic Innervation

NOTES

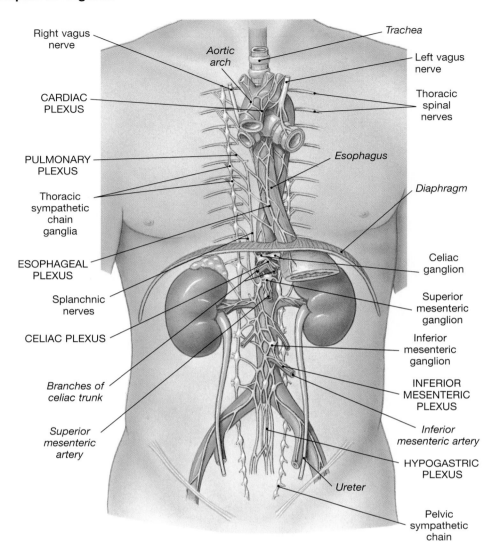

Right vagus
nerve

Trachea

Aortic
arch

Left vagus
nerve

CARDIAC
PLEXUS

Thoracic
spinal
nerves

PULMONARY
PLEXUS

Esophagus

Thoracic
sympathetic
chain
ganglia

Diaphragm

ESOPHAGEAL
PLEXUS

Celiac
ganglion

Splanchnic
nerves

Superior
mesenteric
ganglion

CELIAC PLEXUS

Inferior
mesenteric
ganglion

INFERIOR
MESENTERIC
PLEXUS

Branches of
celiac trunk

Inferior
mesenteric artery

Superior
mesenteric
artery

HYPOGASTRIC
PLEXUS

Ureter

Pelvic
sympathetic
chain

•FIGURE 16-9 The Autonomic Plexuses

NOTES
_____

17　Sensory Function

CHAPTER OUTLINE

CHAPTER OBJECTIVES

1. Distinguish between the general and special senses.
2. Explain why receptors respond to specific stimuli and how the organization of a receptor affects its sensitivity.
3. Identify the receptors for the general senses, and describe how they function.
4. Describe the sensory organs of smell, and trace the olfactory pathways to their destinations in the brain.
5. Describe the sensory organs of taste, and trace the gustatory pathways to their destinations in the brain.
6. Identify the accessory structures of the eye, and explain their functions.
7. Describe the internal structures of the eye, and explain their functions.
8. Explain how we are able to distinguish colors and perceive depth.
9. Explain how light stimulates production of nerve impulses, and trace the visual pathways to their destinations in the brain.
10. Describe the structures of the external and middle ears, and explain how they function.
11. Describe the parts of the inner ear and their roles in equilibrium and hearing.
12. Trace the pathways for the sensations of equilibrium and hearing to their respective destinations in the brain.

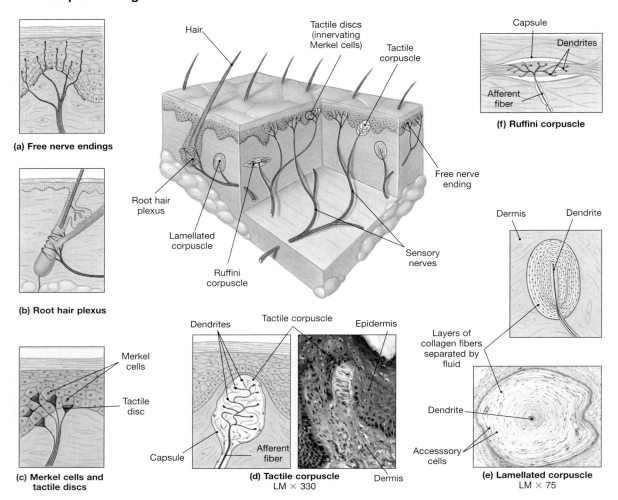

(a) Free nerve endings

(b) Root hair plexus

(c) Merkel cells and tactile discs

Hair

Tactile discs (innervating Merkel cells)

Tactile corpuscle

Root hair plexus

Lamellated corpuscle

Ruffini corpuscle

Free nerve ending

Sensory nerves

Capsule

Dendrites

Afferent fiber

(f) Ruffini corpuscle

Dermis

Dendrite

Layers of collagen fibers separated by fluid

Dendrite

Accesssory cells

(e) Lamellated corpuscle LM × 75

Merkel cells

Tactile disc

Dendrites

Tactile corpuscle

Epidermis

Capsule

Afferent fiber

(d) Tactile corpuscle LM × 330

Dermis

•**FIGURE 17-2** Tactile Receptors in the Skin

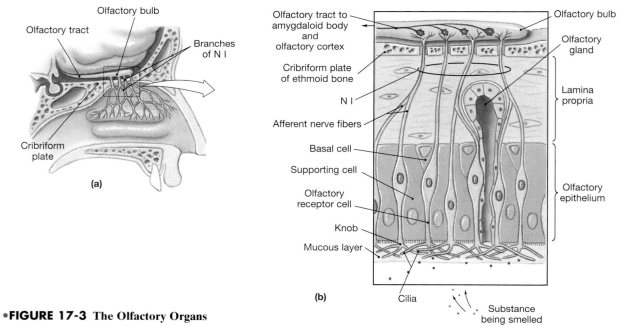

Olfactory bulb

Olfactory tract

Branches of N I

Cribriform plate

(a)

Olfactory tract to amygdaloid body and olfactory cortex

Cribriform plate of ethmoid bone

N I

Afferent nerve fibers

Basal cell

Supporting cell

Olfactory receptor cell

Knob

Mucous layer

Cilia

Substance being smelled

Olfactory bulb

Olfactory gland

Lamina propria

Olfactory epithelium

(b)

•**FIGURE 17-3** The Olfactory Organs

NOTES

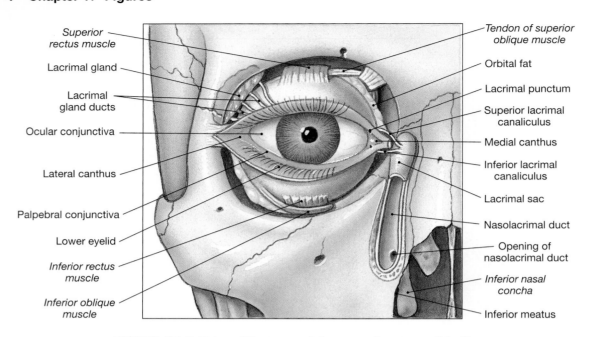

Superior
rectus muscle

Lacrimal gland

Lacrimal
gland ducts

Ocular conjunctiva

Lateral canthus

Palpebral conjunctiva

Lower eyelid

Inferior rectus
muscle

Inferior oblique
muscle

Tendon of superior
oblique muscle

Orbital fat

Lacrimal punctum

Superior lacrimal
canaliculus

Medial canthus

Inferior lacrimal
canaliculus

Lacrimal sac

Nasolacrimal duct

Opening of
nasolacrimal duct

Inferior nasal
concha

Inferior meatus

•**FIGURE 17-5** **External Features and Accessory Structures of the Eye**

NOTES

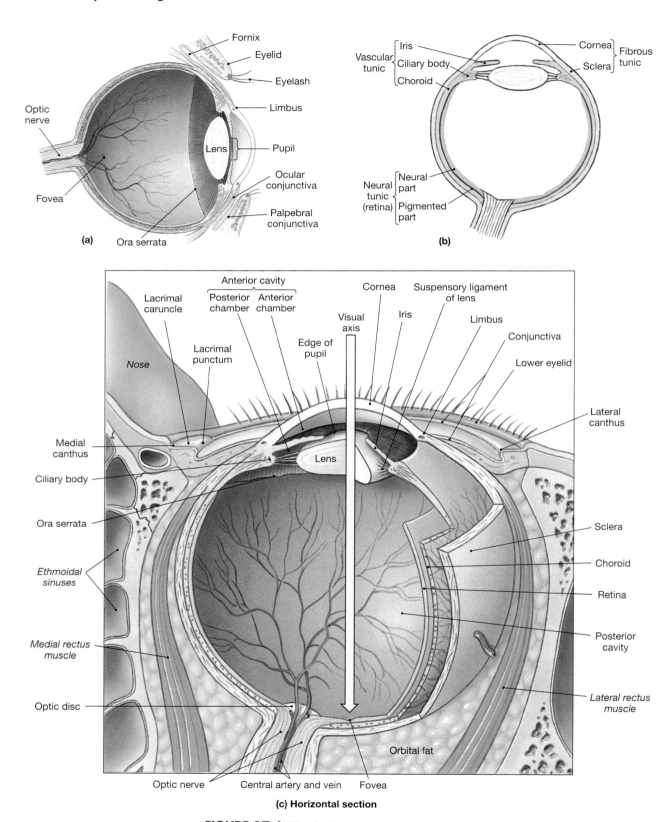

(a)

Fornix
Eyelid
Eyelash
Limbus
Pupil
Ocular conjunctiva
Palpebral conjunctiva
Optic nerve
Fovea
Ora serrata
Lens

(b)

Iris
Vascular tunic
Ciliary body
Choroid
Cornea
Fibrous tunic
Sclera
Neural tunic (retina)
Neural part
Pigmented part

Anterior cavity
Lacrimal caruncle
Posterior chamber
Anterior chamber
Cornea
Suspensory ligament of lens
Visual axis
Iris
Limbus
Conjunctiva
Lower eyelid
Edge of pupil
Nose
Lacrimal punctum
Lateral canthus
Medial canthus
Lens
Ciliary body
Ora serrata
Sclera
Choroid
Ethmoidal sinuses
Retina
Medial rectus muscle
Posterior cavity
Optic disc
Lateral rectus muscle
Orbital fat
Optic nerve
Central artery and vein
Fovea

(c) Horizontal section

•**FIGURE 17-6** The Sectional Anatomy of the Eye

NOTES

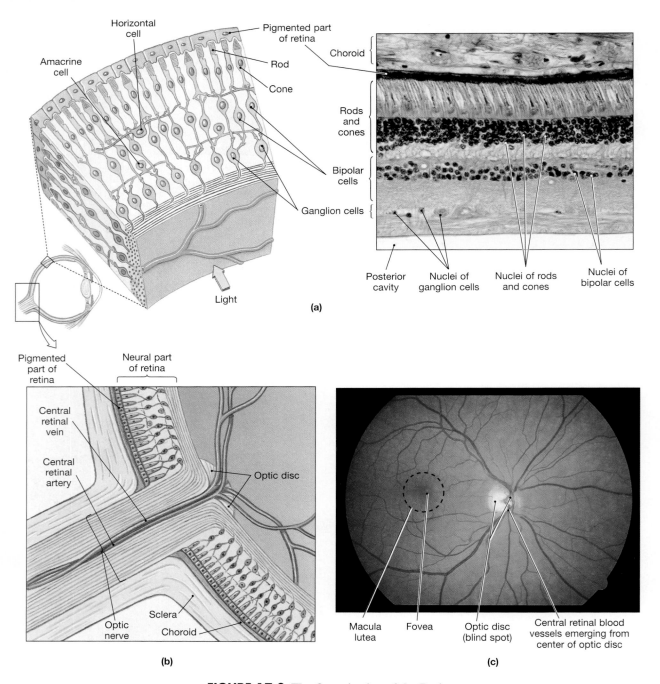

(a)

(b)

(c)

•FIGURE 17-8 The Organization of the Retina

NOTES

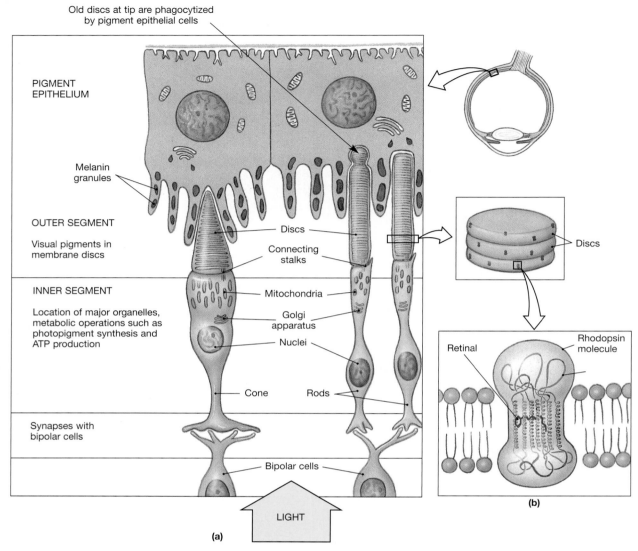

Old discs at tip are phagocytized by pigment epithelial cells

PIGMENT EPITHELIUM

Melanin granules

OUTER SEGMENT

Visual pigments in membrane discs

INNER SEGMENT

Location of major organelles, metabolic operations such as photopigment synthesis and ATP production

Synapses with bipolar cells

Discs

Connecting stalks

Mitochondria

Golgi apparatus

Nuclei

Cone   Rods

Bipolar cells

Discs

Retinal   Rhodopsin molecule

(b)

LIGHT

(a)

•**FIGURE 17-15** Rods and Cones

NOTES

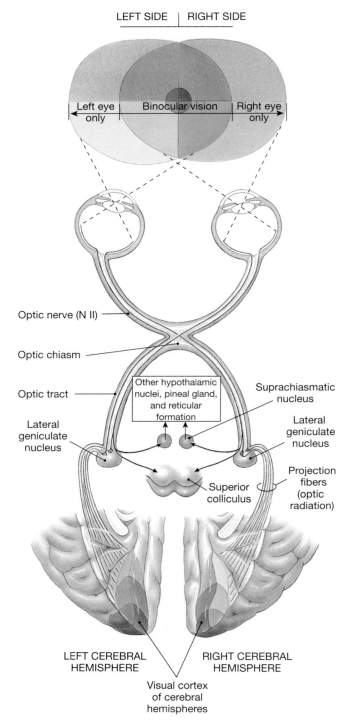

LEFT SIDE | RIGHT SIDE

Left eye only | Binocular vision | Right eye only

Optic nerve (N II)

Optic chiasm

Optic tract

Other hypothalamic nuclei, pineal gland, and reticular formation

Suprachiasmatic nucleus

Lateral geniculate nucleus

Lateral geniculate nucleus

Projection fibers (optic radiation)

Superior colliculus

LEFT CEREBRAL HEMISPHERE

RIGHT CEREBRAL HEMISPHERE

Visual cortex of cerebral hemispheres

•FIGURE 17-21 The Visual Pathways

NOTES

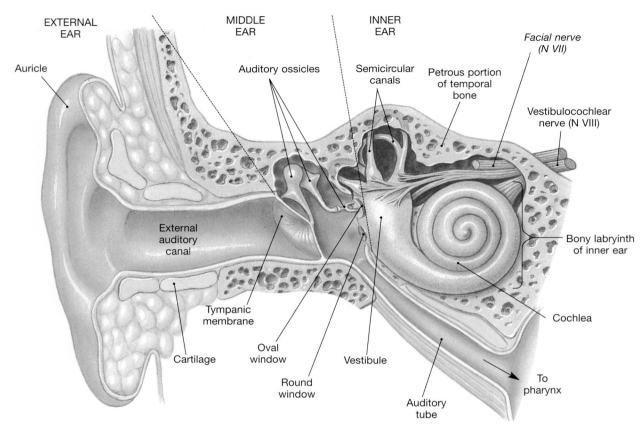

EXTERNAL
EAR

MIDDLE
EAR

INNER
EAR

*Facial nerve
(N VII)*

Auricle

Auditory ossicles

Semicircular
canals

Petrous portion
of temporal
bone

Vestibulocochlear
nerve (N VIII)

External
auditory
canal

Bony labryinth
of inner ear

Cochlea

Tympanic
membrane

Cartilage

Oval
window

Round
window

Vestibule

Auditory
tube

To
pharynx

•FIGURE 17-22 The Anatomy of the Ear

NOTES

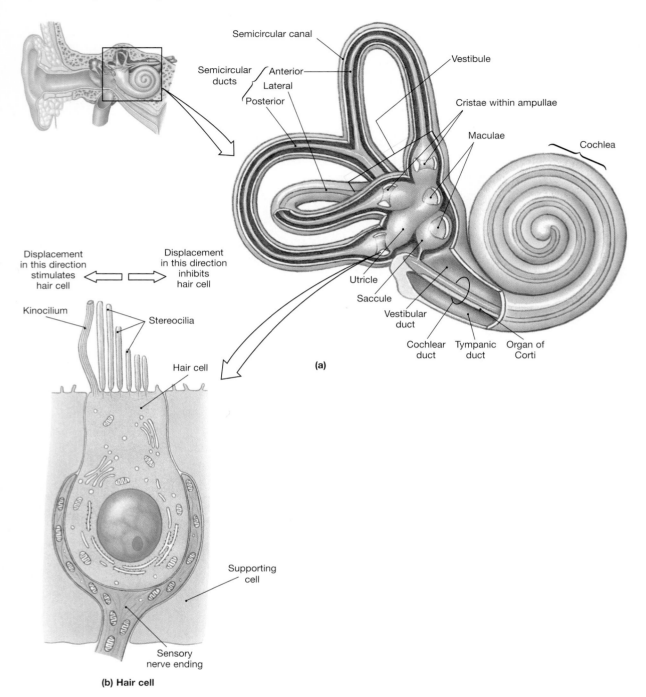

Semicircular canal

Vestibule

Semicircular ducts
Anterior
Lateral
Posterior

Cristae within ampullae

Maculae

Cochlea

Utricle

Saccule

Vestibular duct

Cochlear duct

Tympanic duct

Organ of Corti

(a)

Displacement in this direction stimulates hair cell

Displacement in this direction inhibits hair cell

Kinocilium

Stereocilia

Hair cell

Supporting cell

Sensory nerve ending

(b) Hair cell

•FIGURE 17-24 The Inner Ear

NOTES

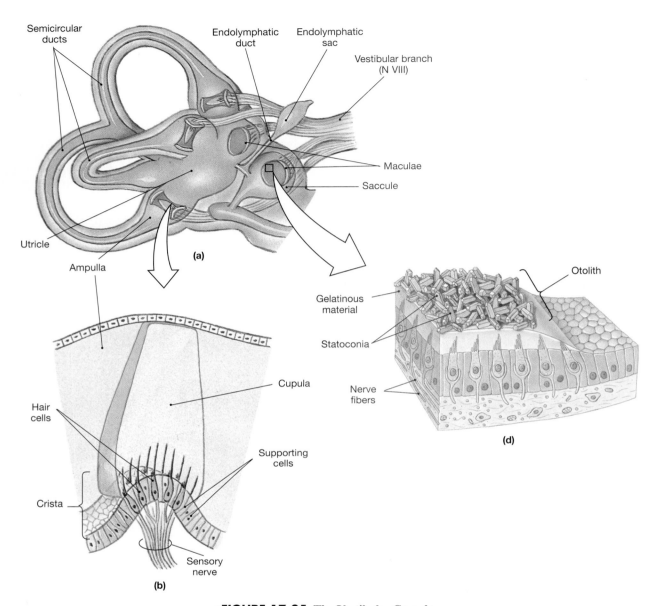

Semicircular ducts

Endolymphatic duct

Endolymphatic sac

Vestibular branch (N VIII)

Maculae

Saccule

Utricle

Ampulla

(a)

Cupula

Hair cells

Supporting cells

Crista

Sensory nerve

(b)

Otolith

Gelatinous material

Statoconia

Nerve fibers

(d)

•**FIGURE 17-25** The Vestibular Complex

NOTES

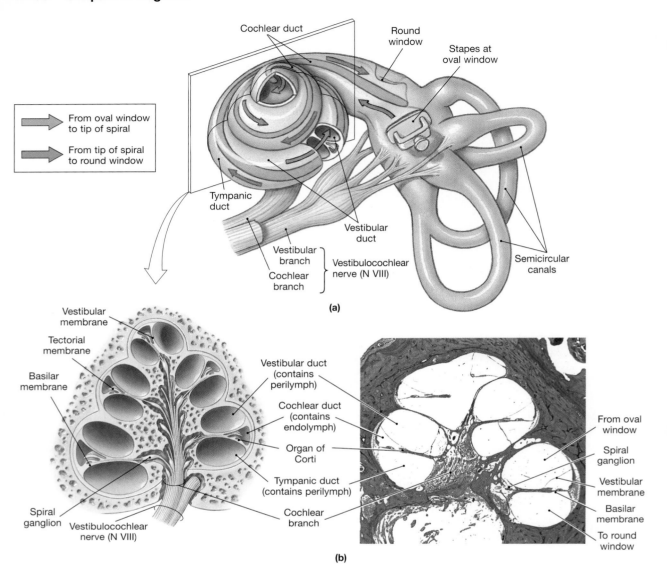

•FIGURE 17-27 The Cochlea

NOTES

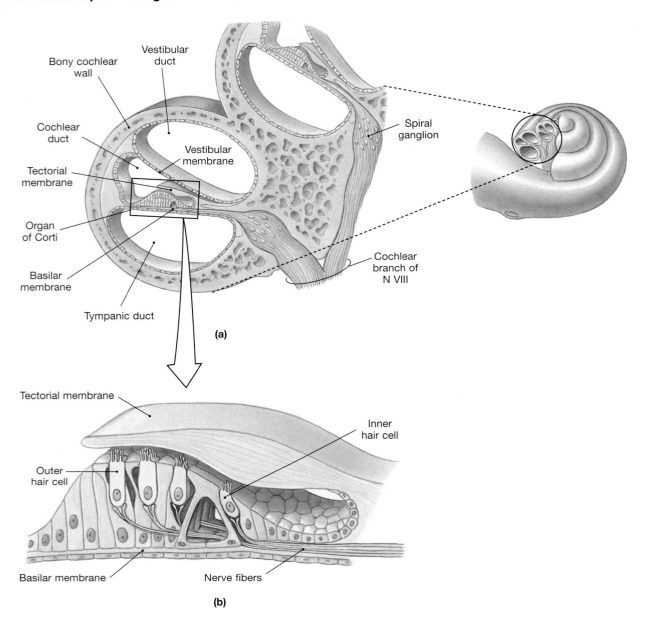

Bony cochlear wall

Vestibular duct

Cochlear duct

Vestibular membrane

Tectorial membrane

Organ of Corti

Basilar membrane

Tympanic duct

Spiral ganglion

Cochlear branch of N VIII

(a)

Tectorial membrane

Inner hair cell

Outer hair cell

Basilar membrane

Nerve fibers

(b)

•**FIGURE 17-28** The Organ of Corti

NOTES

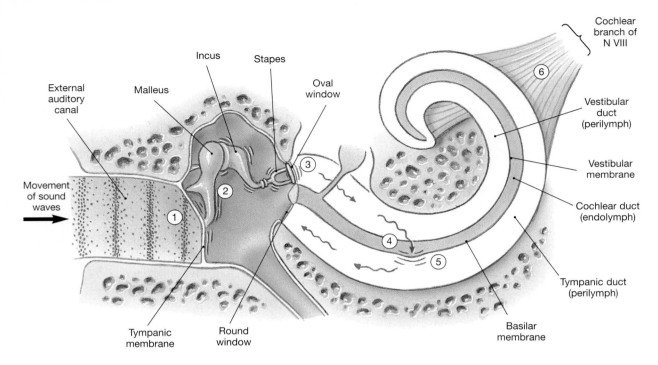

NOTES

18   The Endocrine System

CHAPTER OUTLINE

CHAPTER OBJECTIVES

1. Compare the endocrine and nervous systems.
2. Compare the cellular components of the endocrine system with those of other tissues and systems.
3. Compare the major chemical classes of hormones.
4. Explain the general mechanisms of hormonal action.
5. Describe how endocrine organs are controlled.
6. Describe the location, hormones, and functions of the pituitary gland, thyroid gland, parathyroid glands, adrenal glands, pineal gland, intestines, kidneys, heart, thymus, pancreas, testes, and ovaries.
7. Discuss the results of abnormal levels of hormone production.
8. Explain how hormones interact to produce coordinated physiological responses.
9. Identify the hormones that are especially important to normal growth, and discuss their roles.
10. Define the general adaptation syndrome, and compare homeostatic responses with stress responses.
11. Describe the effects that hormones have on behavior.
12. Give examples of interactions between the endocrine system and each of the other organ systems.

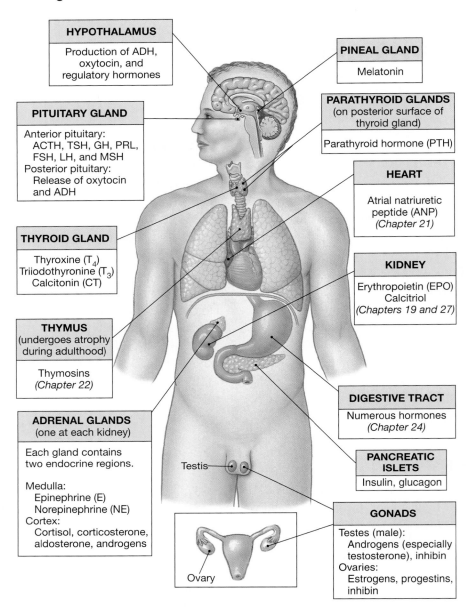

HYPOTHALAMUS

Production of ADH, oxytocin, and regulatory hormones

PINEAL GLAND

Melatonin

PITUITARY GLAND

Anterior pituitary: ACTH, TSH, GH, PRL, FSH, LH, and MSH
Posterior pituitary: Release of oxytocin and ADH

PARATHYROID GLANDS
(on posterior surface of thyroid gland)

Parathyroid hormone (PTH)

HEART

Atrial natriuretic peptide (ANP)
(Chapter 21)

THYROID GLAND

Thyroxine (T$_4$)
Triiodothyronine (T$_3$)
Calcitonin (CT)

KIDNEY

Erythropoietin (EPO)
Calcitriol
(Chapters 19 and 27)

THYMUS
(undergoes atrophy during adulthood)

Thymosins
(Chapter 22)

DIGESTIVE TRACT

Numerous hormones
(Chapter 24)

ADRENAL GLANDS
(one at each kidney)

Each gland contains two endocrine regions.

Medulla:
    Epinephrine (E)
    Norepinephrine (NE)
Cortex:
    Cortisol, corticosterone, aldosterone, androgens

Testis

PANCREATIC ISLETS

Insulin, glucagon

Ovary

GONADS

Testes (male):
    Androgens (especially testosterone), inhibin
Ovaries:
    Estrogens, progestins, inhibin

•**FIGURE 18-1** The Endocrine System

NOTES

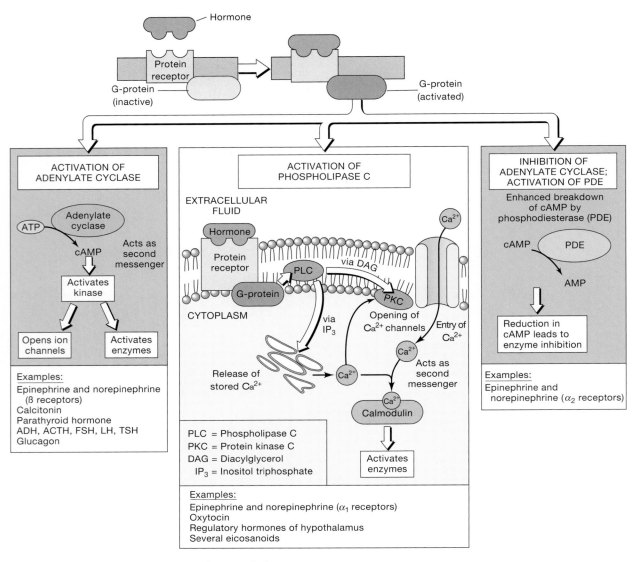

•**FIGURE 18-3** Mechanisms of Hormone Activity

NOTES

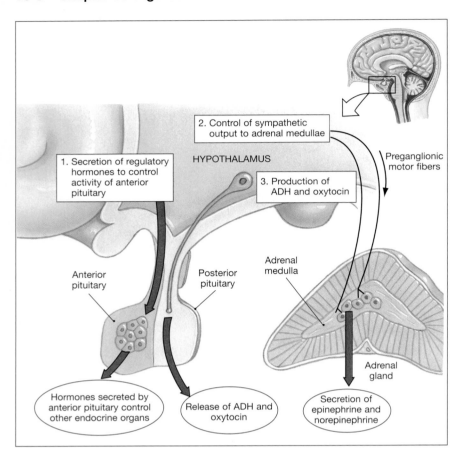

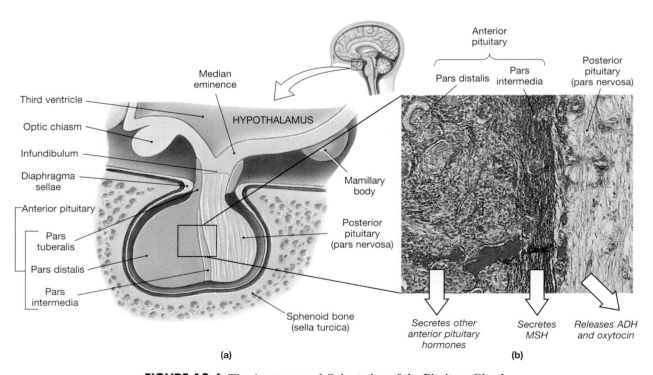

•**FIGURE 18-5** Three Methods of Hypothalamic Control over Endocrine Function

•**FIGURE 18-6** The Anatomy and Orientation of the Pituitary Gland

NOTES

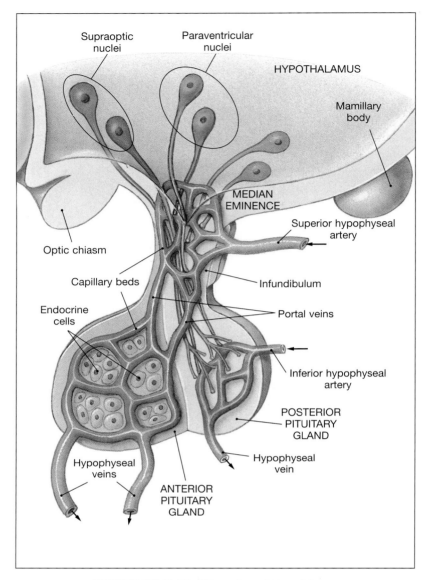

•**FIGURE 18-7** The Hypophyseal Portal System

NOTES

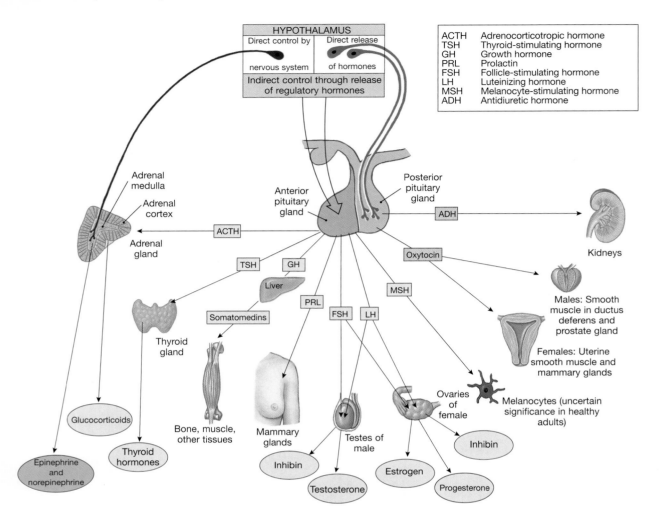

•FIGURE 18-9 Pituitary Hormones and Their Targets

NOTES

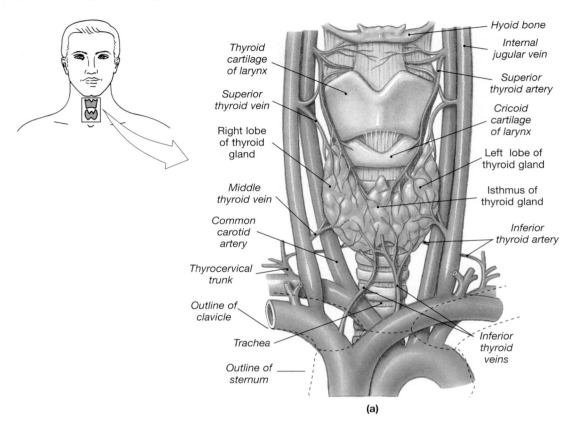

Hyoid bone

Internal
jugular vein

Thyroid
cartilage
of larynx

Superior
thyroid artery

Superior
thyroid vein

Cricoid
cartilage
of larynx

Right lobe
of thyroid
gland

Left lobe of
thyroid gland

Middle
thyroid vein

Isthmus of
thyroid gland

Common
carotid
artery

Inferior
thyroid artery

Thyrocervical
trunk

Outline of
clavicle

Trachea

Inferior
thyroid
veins

Outline of
sternum

(a)

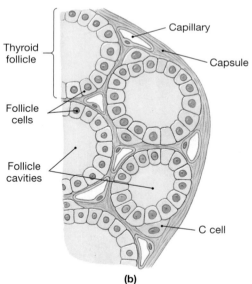

Capillary

Thyroid
follicle

Capsule

Follicle
cells

Follicle
cavities

C cell

(b)

•FIGURE 18-10 The Thyroid Gland

NOTES
_____

•FIGURE 18-11 The Functions of the Thyroid Follicles

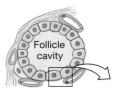

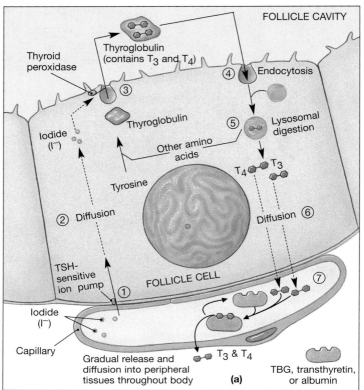

(a)

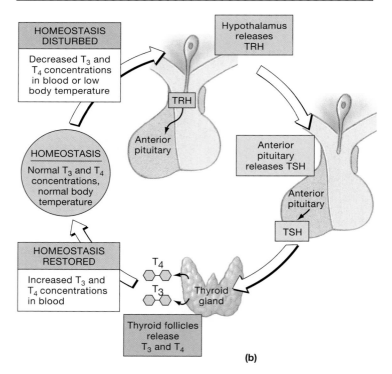

(b)

NOTES

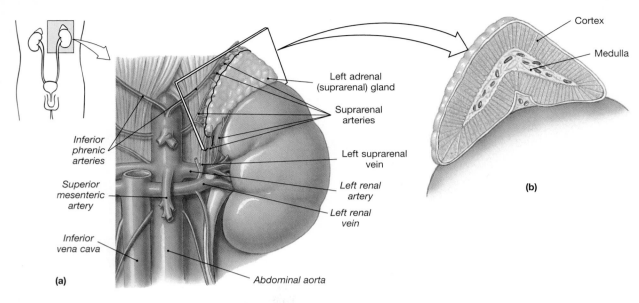

•FIGURE 18-14 The Adrenal Gland

NOTES

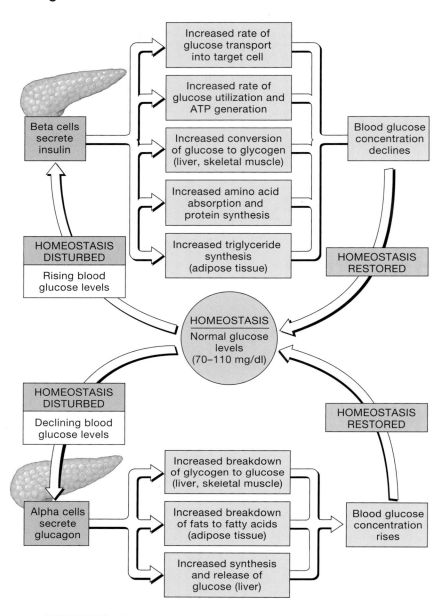

•**FIGURE 18-16** **The Regulation of Blood Glucose Concentrations**

NOTES

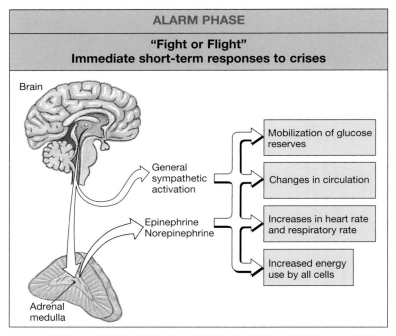

ALARM PHASE

"Fight or Flight"
Immediate short-term responses to crises

Brain

General sympathetic activation

Epinephrine
Norepinephrine

Mobilization of glucose reserves

Changes in circulation

Increases in heart rate and respiratory rate

Increased energy use by all cells

Adrenal medulla

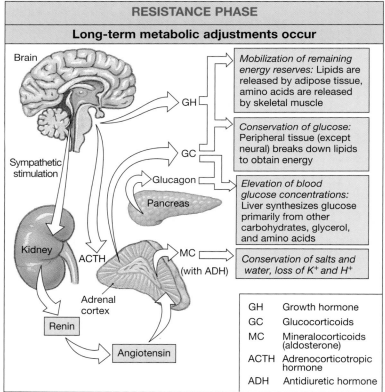

RESISTANCE PHASE

Long-term metabolic adjustments occur

Brain

Sympathetic stimulation

GH

GC

Glucagon

Pancreas

MC
(with ADH)

ACTH

Kidney

Adrenal cortex

Renin

Angiotensin

Mobilization of remaining energy reserves: Lipids are released by adipose tissue, amino acids are released by skeletal muscle

Conservation of glucose: Peripheral tissue (except neural) breaks down lipids to obtain energy

Elevation of blood glucose concentrations: Liver synthesizes glucose primarily from other carbohydrates, glycerol, and amino acids

Conservation of salts and water, loss of K^+ and H^+

GH	Growth hormone
GC	Glucocorticoids
MC	Mineralocorticoids (aldosterone)
ACTH	Adrenocorticotropic hormone
ADH	Antidiuretic hormone

EXHAUSTION PHASE

Collapse of vital systems

Causes may include:
— Exhaustion of lipid reserves
— Inability to produce glucocorticoids
— Failure to maintain electrolyte balance
— Cumulative structural or functional damage to vital organs

•FIGURE 18-17
The General Adaptation Syndrome

NOTES

19   **Blood**

CHAPTER OUTLINE

CHAPTER OBJECTIVES

1. Describe the important components and major functions of blood.
2. Identify locations on the body used for blood collection, and list the basic physical characteristics of the blood samples drawn from these locations.
3. Discuss the composition and functions of plasma.
4. Describe the origin and production of the formed elements in blood.
5. List the characteristics and functions of red blood cells.
6. Describe the structure of hemoglobin, and indicate its functions.
7. Describe the recycling system for aged or damaged red blood cells.
8. Define erythropoiesis, identify the stages involved in red blood cell maturation, and describe the homeostatic regulation of red blood cell production.
9. List examples of important blood tests, and cite the normal values for each test.
10. Explain the importance of blood typing on the basis of ABO and Rh incompatibilities.
11. Categorize the various white blood cells on the basis of their structures and functions, and discuss the factors that regulate the production of each class.
12. Describe the structure, function, and production of platelets.
13. Discuss mechanisms that control blood loss after an injury, and describe the reaction sequences responsible for blood clotting.

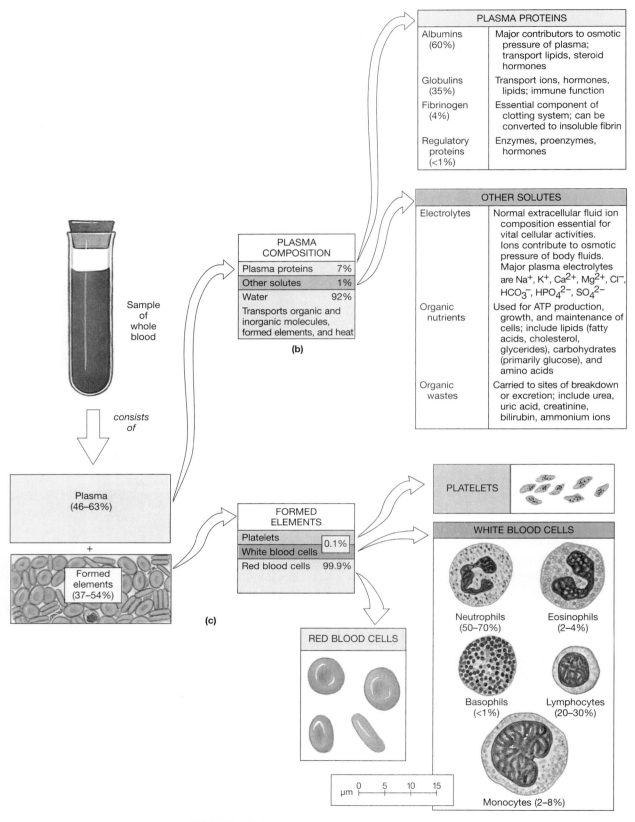

NOTES

•FIGURE 19-3 The Structure of Hemoglobin

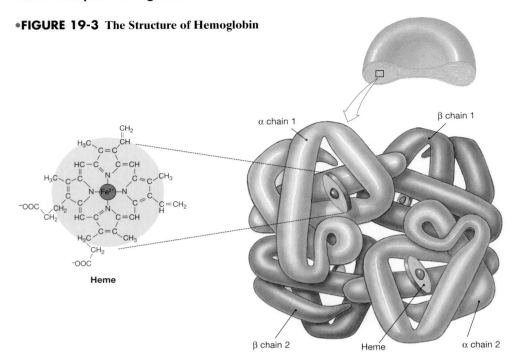

Heme

Hemoglobin molecule

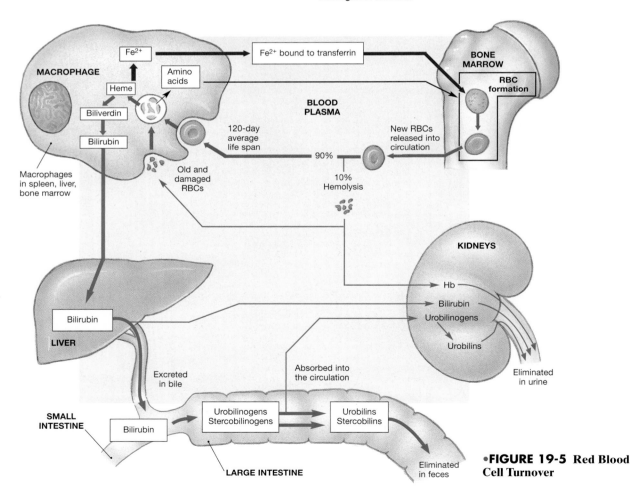

•FIGURE 19-5 Red Blood Cell Turnover

NOTES

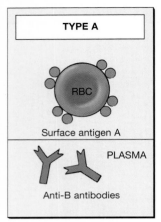
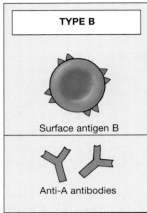
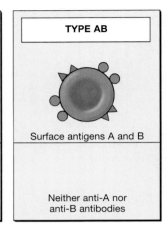
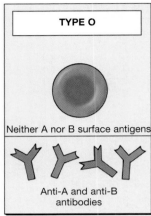

•**FIGURE 19-7** Blood-Typing and Cross-Reactions

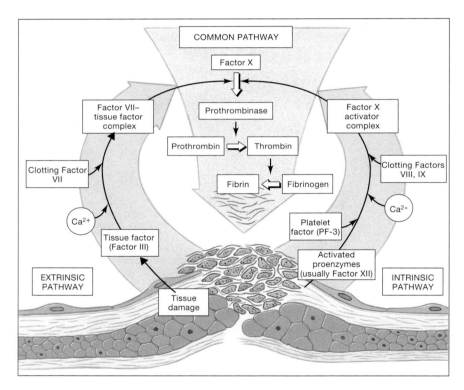

•**FIGURE 19-12** The Coagulation Phase of Hemostasis

NOTES

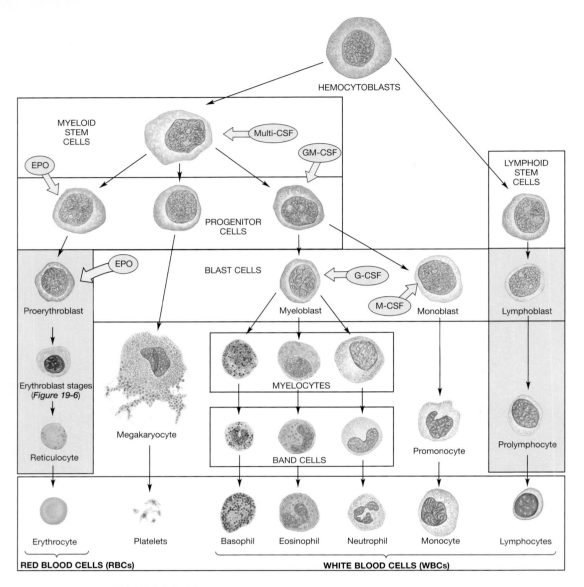

•**FIGURE 19-10** The Origins and Differentiation of Formed Elements

NOTES

CHAPTER

20 **The Heart**

CHAPTER OUTLINE

INTRODUCTION
AN OVERVIEW OF THE CARDIOVASCULAR SYSTEM
ANATOMY OF THE HEART
THE PERICARDIUM
SUPERFICIAL ANATOMY OF THE HEART
THE HEART WALL
INTERNAL ANATOMY AND ORGANIZATION
CONNECTIVE TISSUES AND THE FIBROUS SKELETON
THE BLOOD SUPPLY TO THE HEART
THE HEARTBEAT
CONTRACTILE CELLS
THE CONDUCTING SYSTEM
THE ELECTROCARDIOGRAM
THE CARDIAC CYCLE
CARDIODYNAMICS
OVERVIEW: THE CONTROL OF CARDIAC OUTPUT
FACTORS AFFECTING THE STROKE VOLUME
FACTORS AFFECTING THE HEART RATE
EXERCISE AND CARDIAC OUTPUT
THE HEART AND THE CARDIOVASCULAR SYSTEM

CHAPTER OBJECTIVES

1. Describe the location and general features of the heart.
2. Describe the structure of the pericardium, and explain its functions.
3. Trace the flow of blood through the heart, identifying the major blood vessels, chambers, and heart valves.
4. Identify the layers of the heart wall.
5. Describe the vascular supply to the heart.
6. Describe the events of an action potential in cardiac muscle, and explain the importance of calcium ions to the contractile process.
7. Discuss the differences between nodal cells and conducting cells, and describe the components and functions of the conducting system of the heart.
8. Identify the electrical events associated with a normal electrocardiogram.
9. Explain the events of the cardiac cycle, including atrial and ventricular systole and diastole, and relate the heart sounds to specific events in this cycle.
10. Define stroke volume and cardiac output, and describe the factors that influence these variables.
11. Explain how adjustments in stroke volume and cardiac output are coordinated at different levels of activity.
12. Describe the effects of autonomic innervation on heart function.
13. Describe the effects of hormones on the heart.

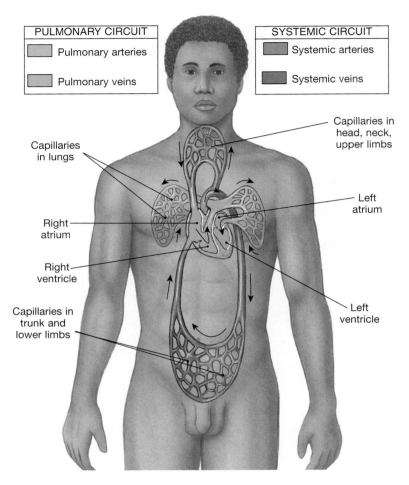

•**FIGURE 20-1** An Overview of the Cardiovascular System

NOTES

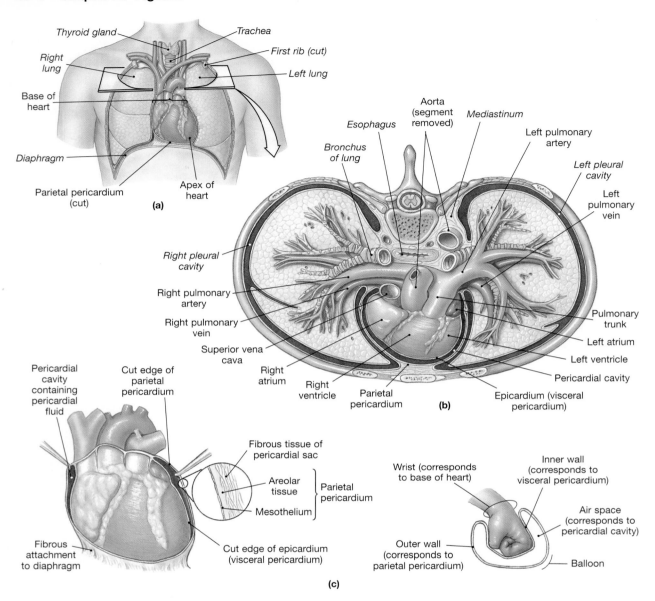

•**FIGURE 20-2** The Location of the Heart in the Thoracic Cavity

NOTES

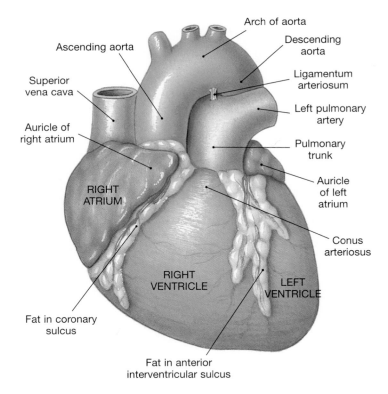

Arch of aorta

Ascending aorta

Descending aorta

Superior vena cava

Ligamentum arteriosum

Left pulmonary artery

Auricle of right atrium

Pulmonary trunk

Auricle of left atrium

RIGHT ATRIUM

Conus arteriosus

RIGHT VENTRICLE

LEFT VENTRICLE

Fat in coronary sulcus

Fat in anterior interventricular sulcus

(a) Anterior surface

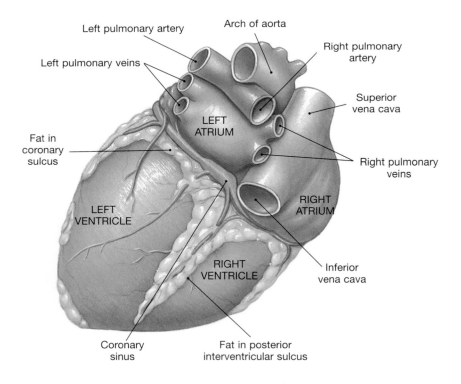

Left pulmonary artery

Arch of aorta

Left pulmonary veins

Right pulmonary artery

LEFT ATRIUM

Superior vena cava

Fat in coronary sulcus

Right pulmonary veins

LEFT VENTRICLE

RIGHT ATRIUM

RIGHT VENTRICLE

Inferior vena cava

Coronary sinus

Fat in posterior interventricular sulcus

(b) Posterior surface

•**FIGURE 20-3** The Superficial Anatomy of the Heart

NOTES

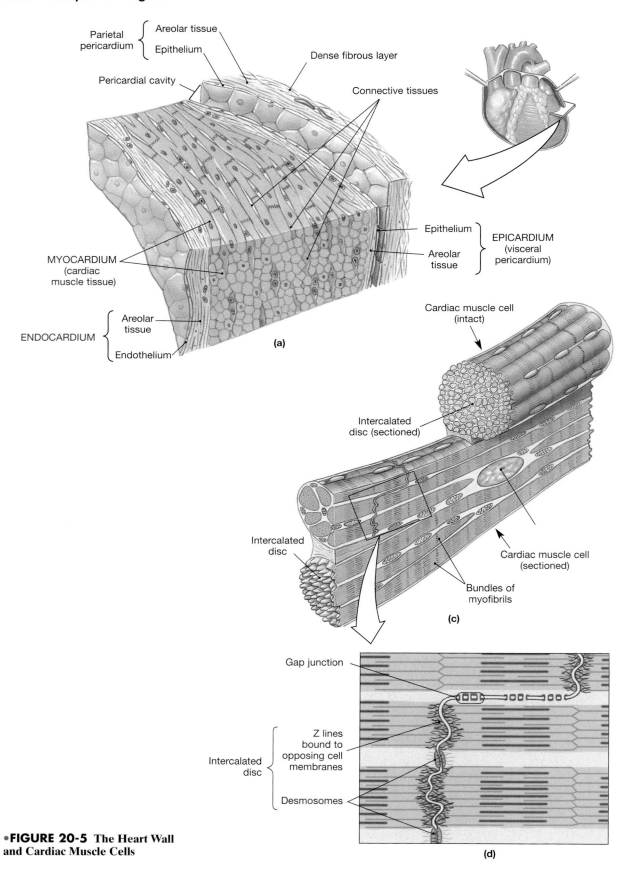

Parietal pericardium { Areolar tissue / Epithelium

Pericardial cavity

Dense fibrous layer

Connective tissues

Epithelium } EPICARDIUM (visceral pericardium)
Areolar tissue

MYOCARDIUM (cardiac muscle tissue)

ENDOCARDIUM { Areolar tissue / Endothelium

(a)

Cardiac muscle cell (intact)

Intercalated disc (sectioned)

Intercalated disc

Cardiac muscle cell (sectioned)

Bundles of myofibrils

(c)

Gap junction

Intercalated disc { Z lines bound to opposing cell membranes / Desmosomes

(d)

•**FIGURE 20-5** The Heart Wall and Cardiac Muscle Cells

NOTES

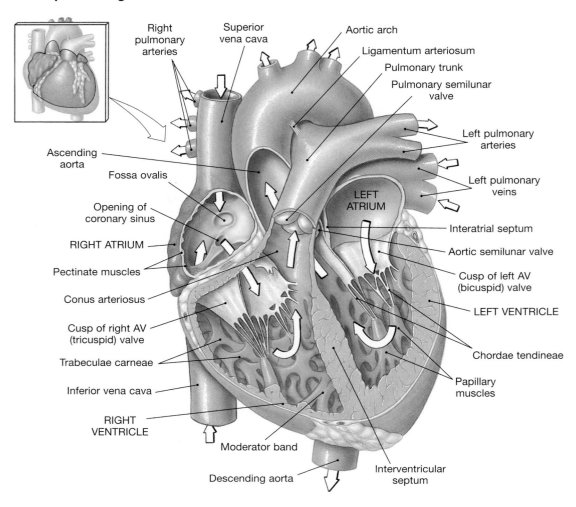

●**FIGURE 20-6** The Sectional Anatomy of the Heart

NOTES

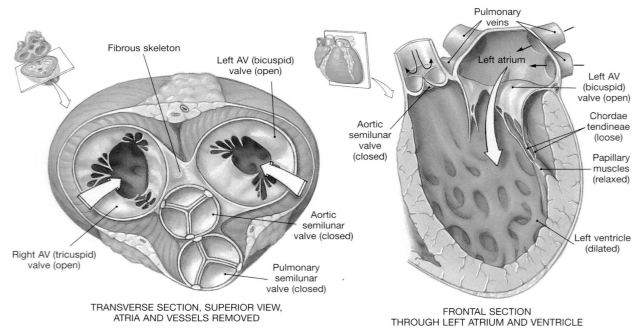

Fibrous skeleton

Left AV (bicuspid) valve (open)

Right AV (tricuspid) valve (open)

Aortic semilunar valve (closed)

Pulmonary semilunar valve (closed)

TRANSVERSE SECTION, SUPERIOR VIEW, ATRIA AND VESSELS REMOVED

Pulmonary veins

Left atrium

Aortic semilunar valve (closed)

Left AV (bicuspid) valve (open)

Chordae tendineae (loose)

Papillary muscles (relaxed)

Left ventricle (dilated)

FRONTAL SECTION THROUGH LEFT ATRIUM AND VENTRICLE

(a) Relaxed ventricles

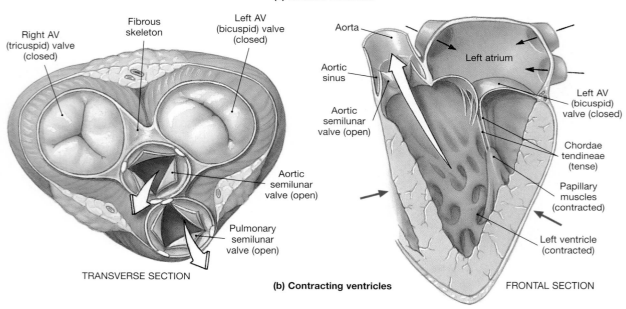

Right AV (tricuspid) valve (closed)

Fibrous skeleton

Left AV (bicuspid) valve (closed)

Aortic semilunar valve (open)

Pulmonary semilunar valve (open)

TRANSVERSE SECTION

Aorta

Aortic sinus

Aortic semilunar valve (open)

Left atrium

Left AV (bicuspid) valve (closed)

Chordae tendineae (tense)

Papillary muscles (contracted)

Left ventricle (contracted)

FRONTAL SECTION

(b) Contracting ventricles

•**FIGURE 20-8** Valves of the Heart

NOTES

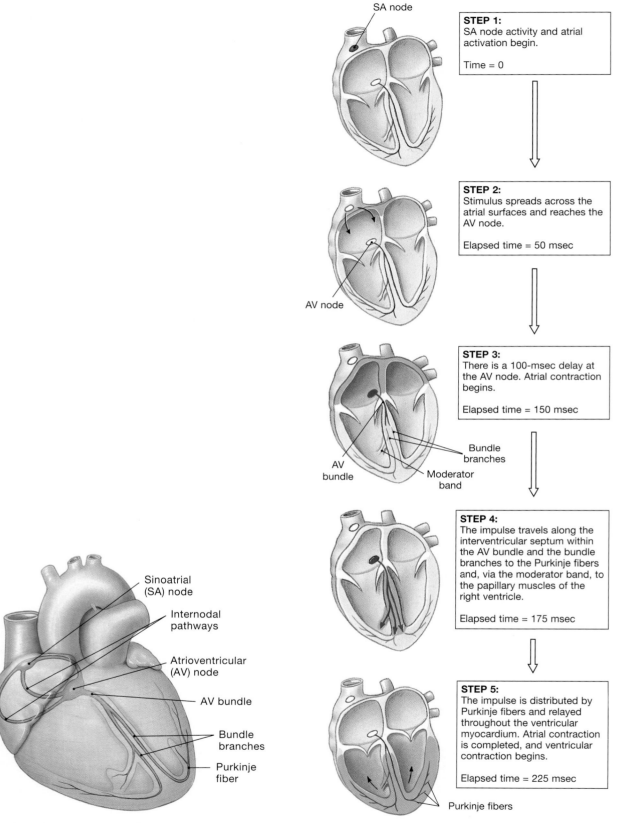

STEP 1:
SA node activity and atrial activation begin.

Time = 0

STEP 2:
Stimulus spreads across the atrial surfaces and reaches the AV node.

Elapsed time = 50 msec

AV node

STEP 3:
There is a 100-msec delay at the AV node. Atrial contraction begins.

Elapsed time = 150 msec

Bundle branches

AV bundle

Moderator band

STEP 4:
The impulse travels along the interventricular septum within the AV bundle and the bundle branches to the Purkinje fibers and, via the moderator band, to the papillary muscles of the right ventricle.

Elapsed time = 175 msec

STEP 5:
The impulse is distributed by Purkinje fibers and relayed throughout the ventricular myocardium. Atrial contraction is completed, and ventricular contraction begins.

Elapsed time = 225 msec

Purkinje fibers

SA node

Sinoatrial (SA) node

Internodal pathways

Atrioventricular (AV) node

AV bundle

Bundle branches

Purkinje fiber

•**FIGURE 20-12** The Conducting System of the Heart

•**FIGURE 20-13** Impulse Conduction through the Heart

NOTES

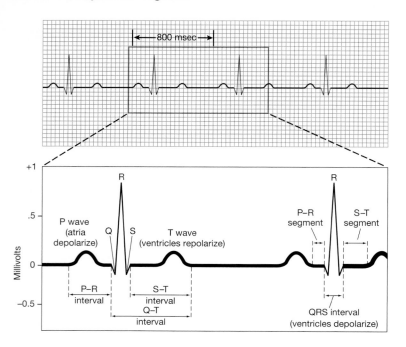

•FIGURE 20-14 An Electrocardiogram

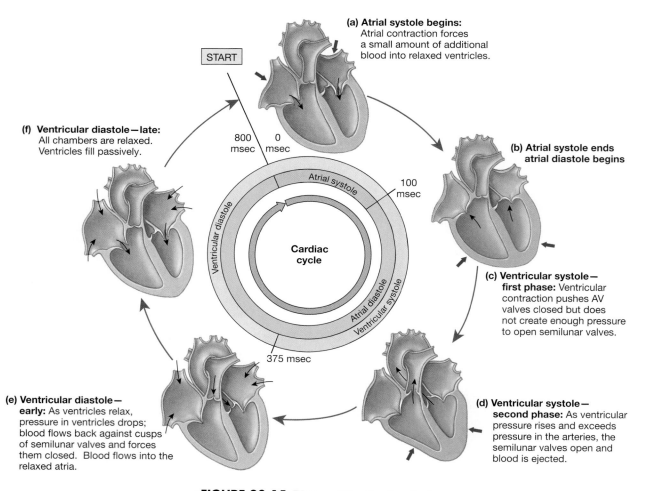

(a) Atrial systole begins: Atrial contraction forces a small amount of additional blood into relaxed ventricles.

START

(b) Atrial systole ends atrial diastole begins

(c) Ventricular systole— first phase: Ventricular contraction pushes AV valves closed but does not create enough pressure to open semilunar valves.

(d) Ventricular systole— second phase: As ventricular pressure rises and exceeds pressure in the arteries, the semilunar valves open and blood is ejected.

(e) Ventricular diastole— early: As ventricles relax, pressure in ventricles drops; blood flows back against cusps of semilunar valves and forces them closed. Blood flows into the relaxed atria.

(f) Ventricular diastole—late: All chambers are relaxed. Ventricles fill passively.

Cardiac cycle

Atrial systole
Ventricular diastole
Atrial diastole
Ventricular systole

800 msec
0 msec
100 msec
375 msec

•FIGURE 20-15 Phases of the Cardiac Cycle

© 2002 Prentice Hall, Inc.

NOTES

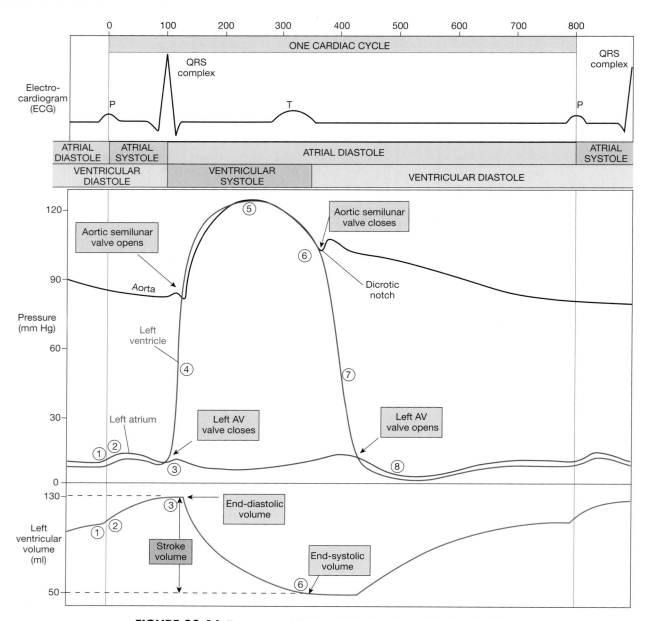

•**FIGURE 20-16** Pressure and Volume Relationships in the Cardiac Cycle

NOTES

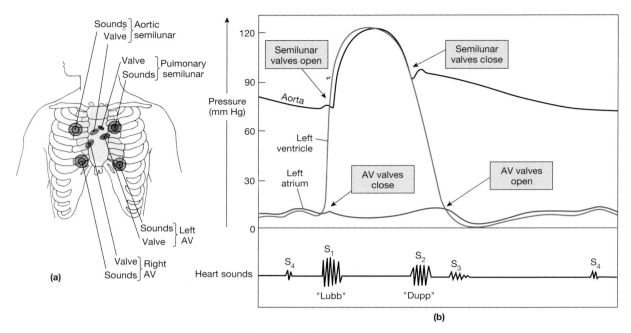

•**FIGURE 20-17** Heart Sounds

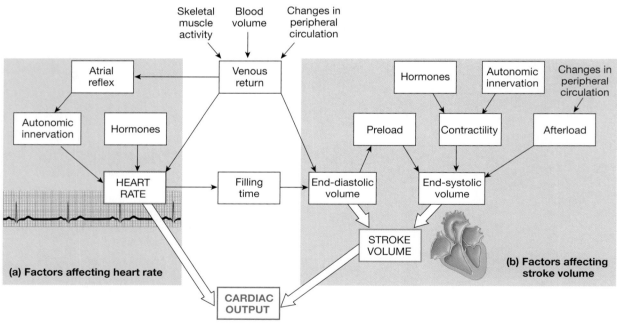

•**FIGURE 20-22** Factors Affecting Cardiac Output

NOTES

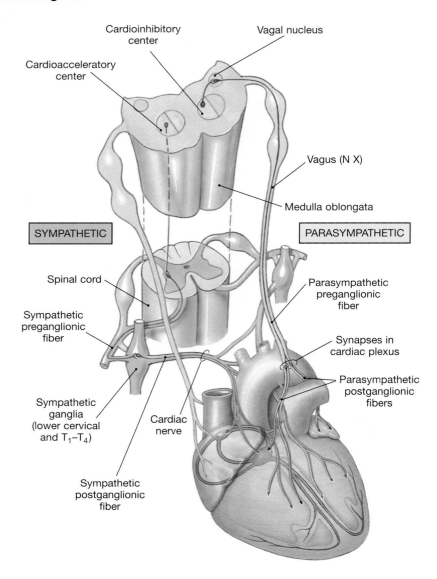

Cardioinhibitory center

Vagal nucleus

Cardioacceleratory center

Vagus (N X)

Medulla oblongata

SYMPATHETIC

PARASYMPATHETIC

Spinal cord

Parasympathetic preganglionic fiber

Sympathetic preganglionic fiber

Synapses in cardiac plexus

Parasympathetic postganglionic fibers

Sympathetic ganglia (lower cervical and T₁–T₄)

Cardiac nerve

Sympathetic postganglionic fiber

•**FIGURE 20-20** Autonomic Innervation of the Heart

NOTES

21 Blood Vessels and Circulation

CHAPTER OUTLINE

CHAPTER OBJECTIVES

1. Distinguish among the types of blood vessels on the basis of their structure and function.
2. Describe how and where fluid and dissolved materials enter and leave the cardiovascular system.
3. Explain the mechanisms that regulate blood flow through arteries, capillaries, and veins.
4. Describe the factors that influence blood pressure and how blood pressure is regulated.
5. Discuss the mechanisms and various pressures involved in the movement of fluids between capillaries and interstitial spaces.
6. Describe how central and local control mechanisms interact to regulate blood flow and pressure in tissues.
7. Explain how the activities of the cardiac, vasomotor, and respiratory centers are coordinated to control blood flow through the tissues.
8. Explain how the cardiovascular system responds to the demands of exercise, hemorrhaging, and shock.
9. Identify the principal blood vessels and the functional characteristics of the special circulation to the brain, heart, and lungs.
10. Identify the major arteries and veins and the areas they serve.
11. Discuss the effects of aging on the cardiovascular system.
12. Give examples of interactions between the cardiovascular system and each of the other organ systems.

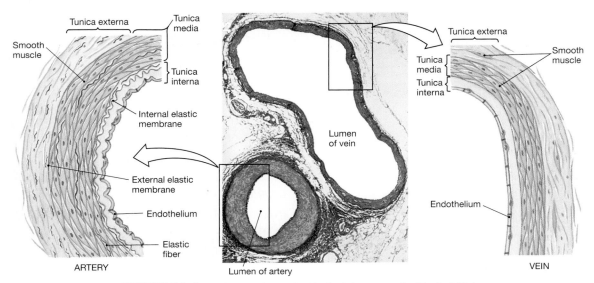

•**FIGURE 21-1** A Comparison of a Typical Artery and a Typical Vein

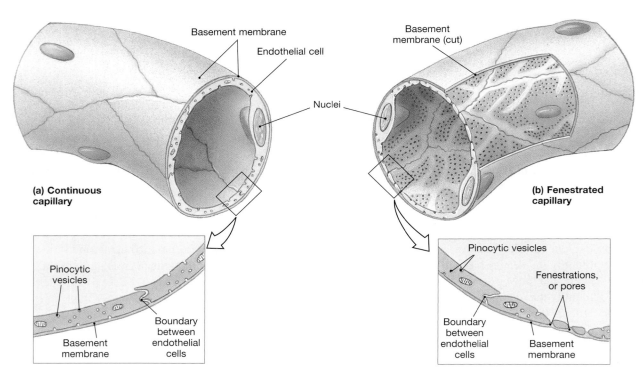

•**FIGURE 21-3** Capillary Structure

NOTES

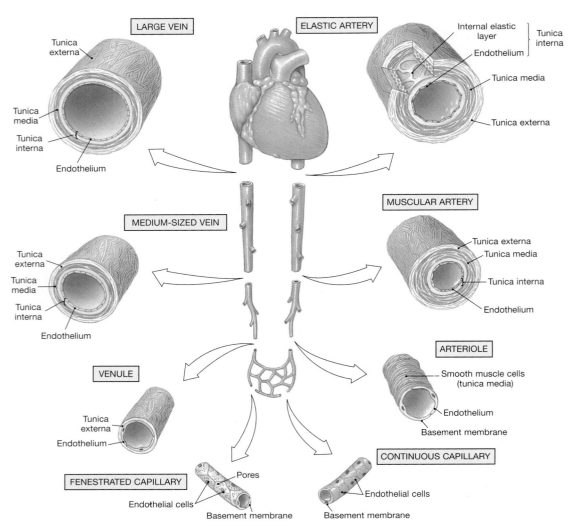

•**FIGURE 21-2** Histological Structure of Blood Vessels

NOTES

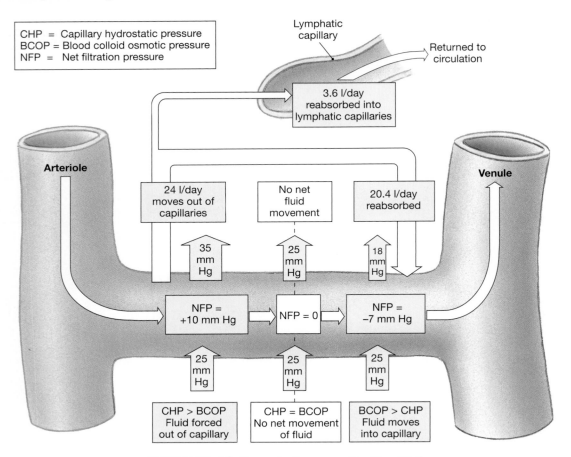

•**FIGURE 21-13** Forces Acting across Capillary Walls

NOTES

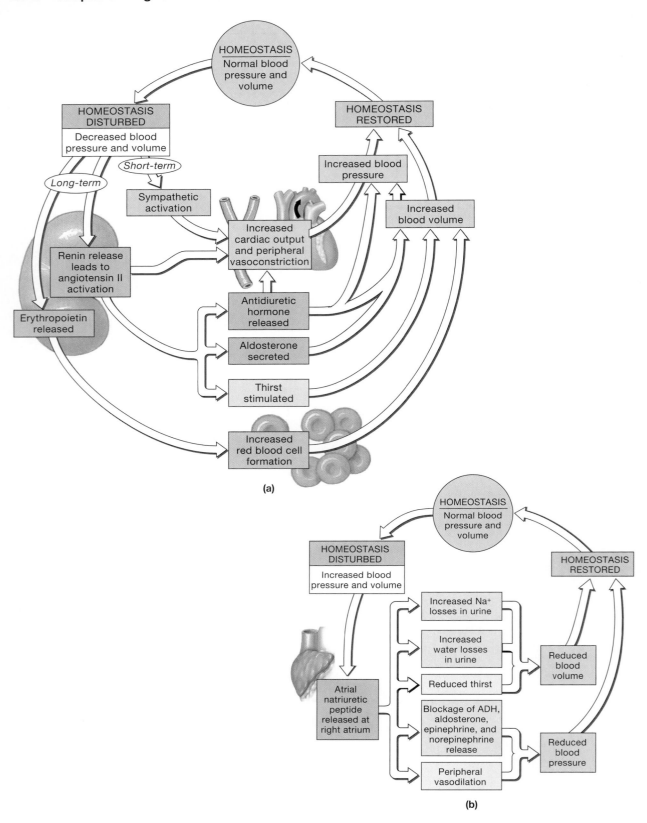

(a)

(b)

•FIGURE 21-17 The Regulation of Blood Pressure and Blood Volume

NOTES

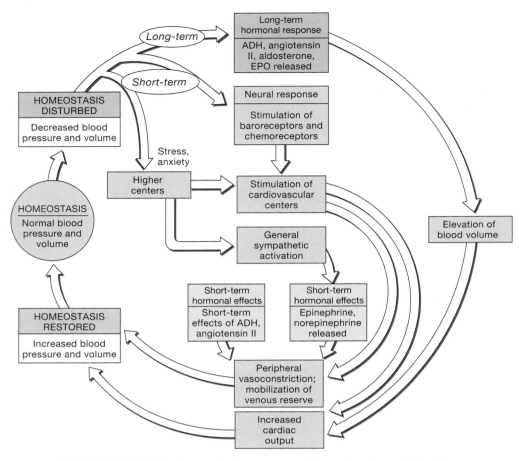

•**FIGURE 21-18** Cardiovascular Responses to Hemorrhaging and Blood Loss

NOTES

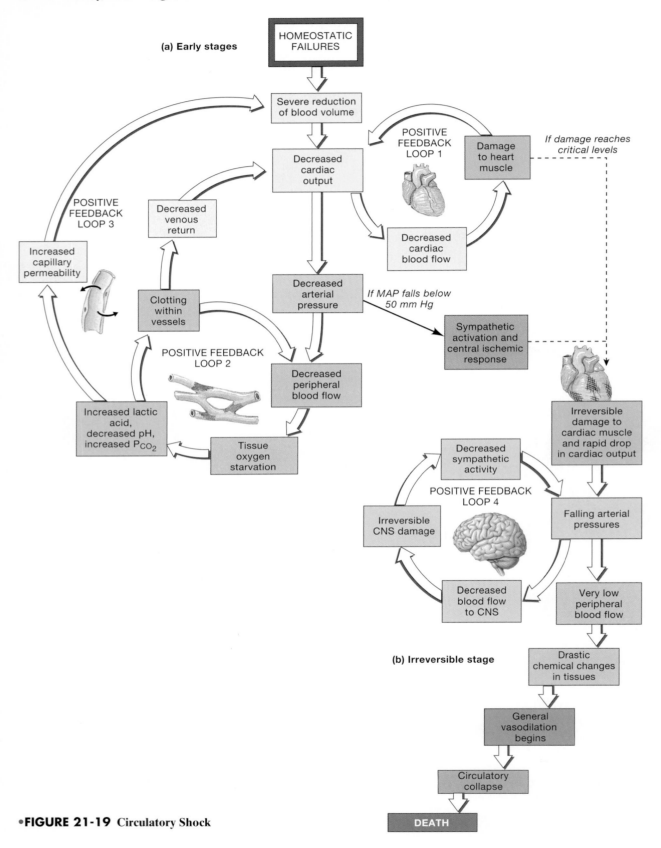

•**FIGURE 21-19** Circulatory Shock

NOTES

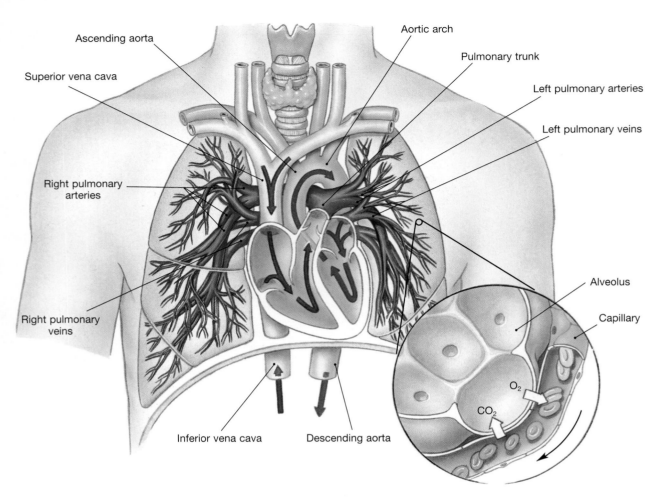

•**FIGURE 21-21** The Pulmonary Circuit

NOTES
_____

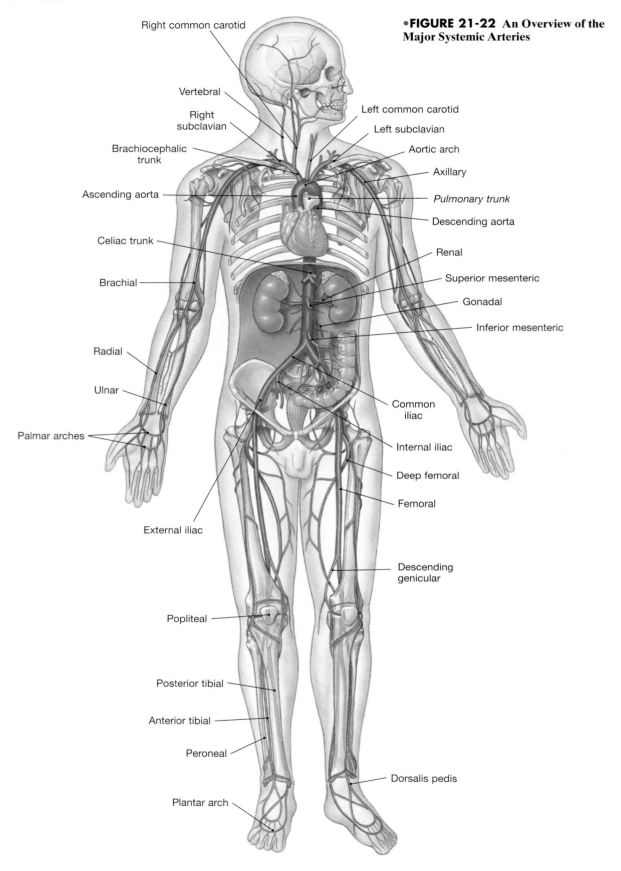

•**FIGURE 21-22** An Overview of the
Major Systemic Arteries

Right common carotid

Vertebral

Right
subclavian

Brachiocephalic
trunk

Ascending aorta

Celiac trunk

Brachial

Radial

Ulnar

Palmar arches

External iliac

Popliteal

Posterior tibial

Anterior tibial

Peroneal

Plantar arch

Left common carotid

Left subclavian

Aortic arch

Axillary

Pulmonary trunk

Descending aorta

Renal

Superior mesenteric

Gonadal

Inferior mesenteric

Common
iliac

Internal iliac

Deep femoral

Femoral

Descending
genicular

Dorsalis pedis

© 2002 Prentice Hall, Inc.

NOTES

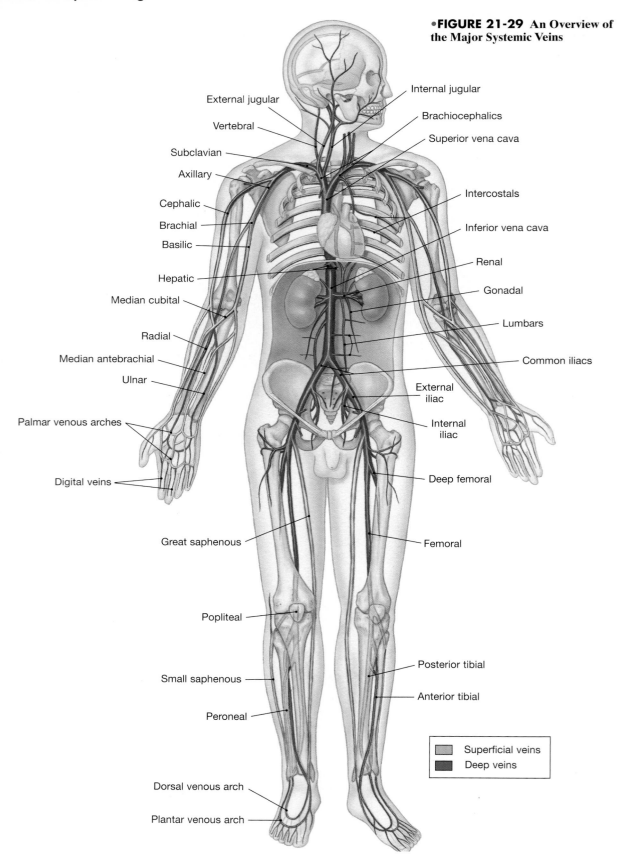

•FIGURE 21-29 An Overview of the Major Systemic Veins

NOTES

22 The Lymphatic System and Immunity

CHAPTER OUTLINE

INTRODUCTION
AN OVERVIEW OF THE LYMPHATIC SYSTEM
ORGANIZATION OF THE LYMPHATIC SYSTEM
FUNCTIONS OF THE LYMPHATIC SYSTEM
LYMPHATIC VESSELS
LYMPHOCYTES
LYMPHOID TISSUES
LYMPHOID ORGANS
THE LYMPHATIC SYSTEM AND BODY DEFENSES
NONSPECIFIC DEFENSES
PHYSICAL BARRIERS
PHAGOCYTES
IMMUNOLOGICAL SURVEILLANCE
INTERFERONS
COMPLEMENT
INFLAMMATION
FEVER
SPECIFIC DEFENSES: THE IMMUNE RESPONSE

FORMS OF IMMUNITY
PROPERTIES OF IMMUNITY
OVERVIEW: THE IMMUNE RESPONSE
T CELLS AND CELL-MEDIATED IMMUNITY
B CELLS AND ANTIBODY-MEDIATED IMMUNITY
PRIMARY AND SECONDARY RESPONSES TO ANTIGEN
    EXPOSURE
HORMONES OF THE IMMUNE SYSTEM
SUMMARY: THE IMMUNE RESPONSE
THE DEVELOPMENT OF RESISTANCE
IMMUNE DISORDERS
AUTOIMMUNE DISORDERS
IMMUNODEFICIENCY DISEASES
ALLERGIES
STRESS AND THE IMMUNE RESPONSE
AGING AND THE IMMUNE RESPONSE
INTEGRATION WITH OTHER SYSTEMS

CHAPTER OBJECTIVES

1. Identify the major components of the lymphatic system, and explain their functions.
2. Discuss the importance of lymphocytes, and describe their distribution in the body.
3. Describe the structure of lymphoid tissues and organs, and explain their functions.
4. List the body's nonspecific defenses, and describe the components and mechanisms of each.
5. Define specific resistance, and identify the forms and properties of immunity.
6. Distinguish between cell-mediated (cellular) immunity and antibody-mediated (humoral) immunity, and identify the cells responsible for each.
7. Discuss the types of T cells and the role played by each in the immune response.
8. Describe the structure of an antibody, and discuss the types of antibodies in body fluids and secretions.
9. Explain the effects of antibodies and how these effects are produced.
10. Discuss the primary and secondary responses to antigen exposure.
11. Discuss important hormones of the immune response and explain their significance.
12. Describe the origin, development, activation, and regulation of resistance.
13. Explain the origin of autoimmune disorders, immunodeficiency diseases, and allergies, and list important examples of each type of disorder.
14. Give examples of interactions between the lymphatic system and each of the other organ systems.

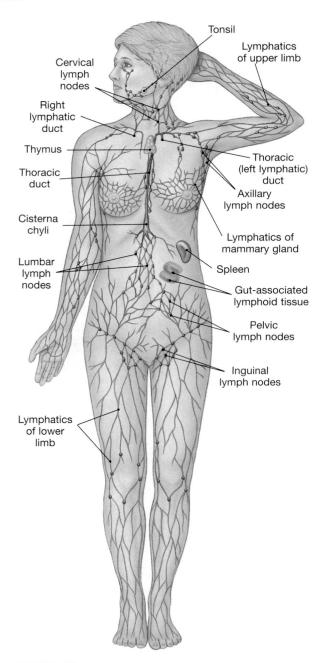

Tonsil

Lymphatics
of upper limb

Cervical
lymph
nodes

Right
lymphatic
duct

Thymus

Thoracic
duct

Cisterna
chyli

Lumbar
lymph
nodes

Thoracic
(left lymphatic)
duct

Axillary
lymph nodes

Lymphatics of
mammary gland

Spleen

Gut-associated
lymphoid tissue

Pelvic
lymph nodes

Inguinal
lymph nodes

Lymphatics
of lower
limb

•FIGURE 22-1 The Components of the Lymphatic System

NOTES

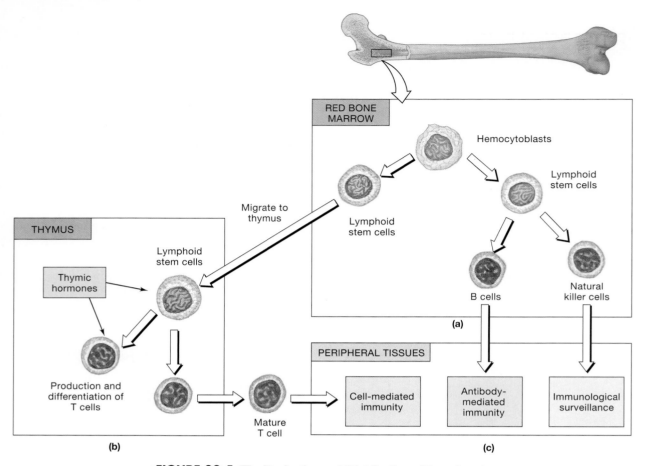

•FIGURE 22-5 The Derivation and Distribution of Lymphocytes

NOTES

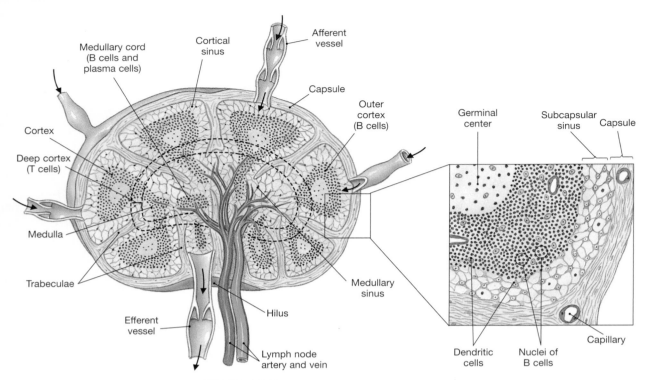

•FIGURE 22-7 The Structure of a Lymph Node

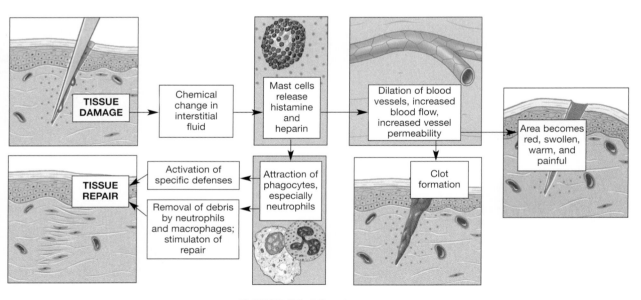

•FIGURE 22-13 Inflammation

NOTES

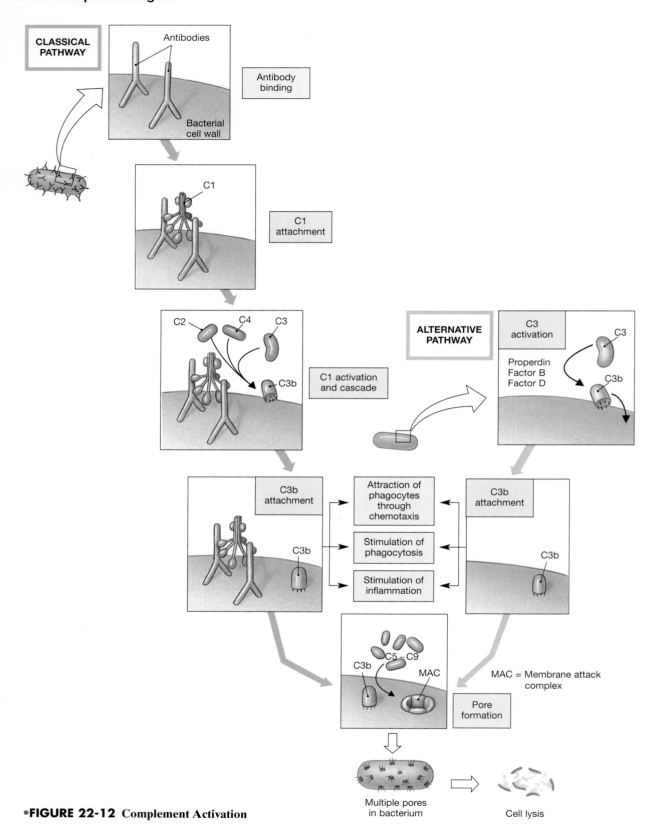

•FIGURE 22-12 Complement Activation

NOTES

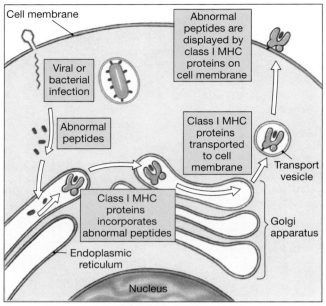

(a) Infected cell

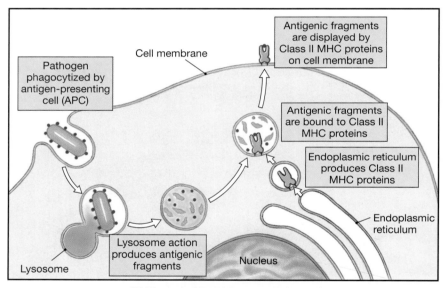

(b) Phagocytic antigen-presenting cell

•FIGURE 22-16 Antigens and Class II MHC Proteins

NOTES

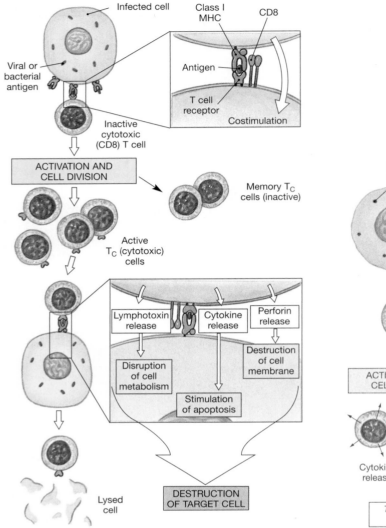

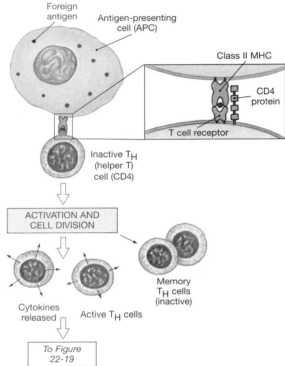

•**FIGURE 22-17** **Antigen Recognition and the Activation of Cytotoxic T Cells**

•**FIGURE 22-18** **Antigen Recognition and Activation of Helper T Cells**

NOTES

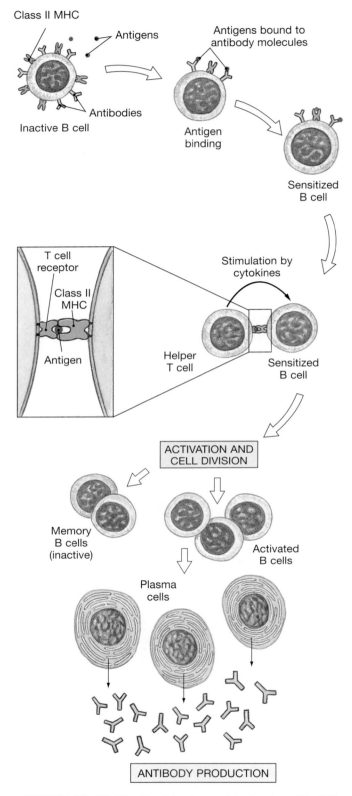

Class II MHC

Antigens

Antigens bound to
antibody molecules

Antibodies

Inactive B cell

Antigen
binding

Sensitized
B cell

T cell
receptor

Class II
MHC

Antigen

Stimulation by
cytokines

Helper
T cell

Sensitized
B cell

ACTIVATION AND
CELL DIVISION

Memory
B cells
(inactive)

Activated
B cells

Plasma
cells

ANTIBODY PRODUCTION

•FIGURE 22-19 The Sensitization and Activation of B Cells

NOTES

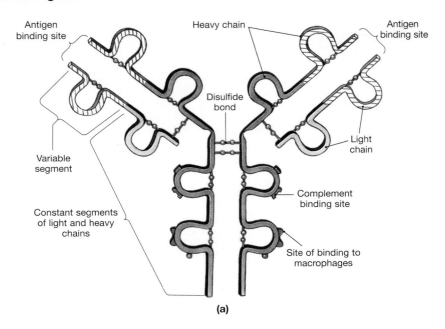

Antigen binding site

Heavy chain

Antigen binding site

Disulfide bond

Variable segment

Light chain

Complement binding site

Constant segments of light and heavy chains

Site of binding to macrophages

(a)

•FIGURE 22-20 Antibody Structure

NOTES

23 The Respiratory System

CHAPTER OUTLINE

CHAPTER OBJECTIVES

1. Describe the primary functions of the respiratory system.
2. Explain how the delicate respiratory exchange surfaces are protected from pathogens, debris, and other hazards.
3. Identify the organs of the upper respiratory system, and describe their functions.
4. Describe the structure of the larynx, and discuss its role in normal breathing and sound production.
5. Discuss the structure of the extrapulmonary airways.
6. Describe the superficial anatomy of the lungs, the structure of a pulmonary lobule, and the functional anatomy of the alveoli.
7. Describe the physical principles governing the movement of air into the lungs and the diffusion of gases into and out of the blood.
8. Describe the origins and actions of the respiratory muscles responsible for respiratory movements.
9. Differentiate between pulmonary ventilation and alveolar ventilation.
10. Describe how oxygen and carbon dioxide are transported in blood.
11. Describe the factors that influence the respiration rate.
12. Identify and discuss reflex respiratory activity and the brain centers involved in the control of respiration.
13. Give examples of interactions between the respiratory system and each of the other organ systems.

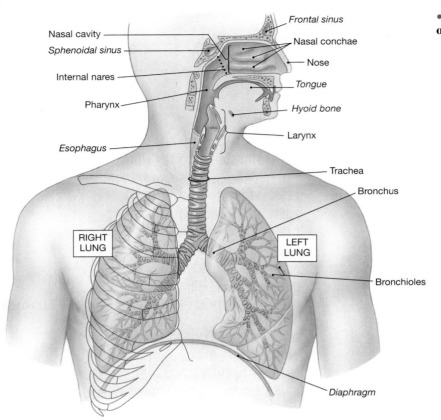

•FIGURE 23-1 The Components of the Respiratory System

Frontal sinus
Nasal cavity
Nasal conchae
Sphenoidal sinus
Nose
Internal nares
Tongue
Pharynx
Hyoid bone
Esophagus
Larynx
Trachea
Bronchus
RIGHT LUNG
LEFT LUNG
Bronchioles
Diaphragm

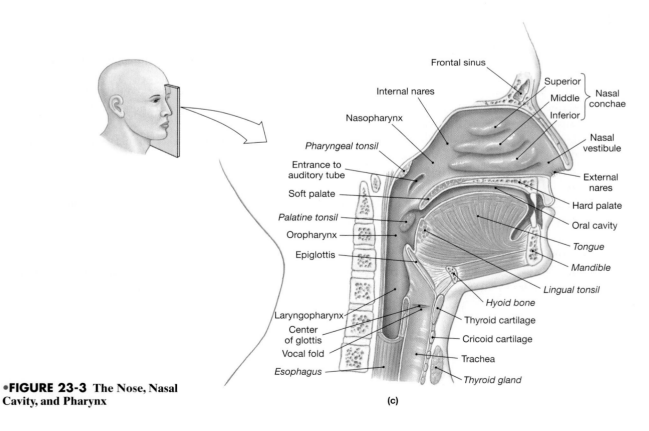

Frontal sinus
Internal nares
Superior
Middle
Inferior
Nasal conchae
Nasopharynx
Pharyngeal tonsil
Nasal vestibule
Entrance to auditory tube
External nares
Soft palate
Hard palate
Palatine tonsil
Oral cavity
Oropharynx
Tongue
Epiglottis
Mandible
Lingual tonsil
Hyoid bone
Laryngopharynx
Thyroid cartilage
Center of glottis
Cricoid cartilage
Vocal fold
Trachea
Esophagus
Thyroid gland

(c)

•FIGURE 23-3 The Nose, Nasal Cavity, and Pharynx

NOTES

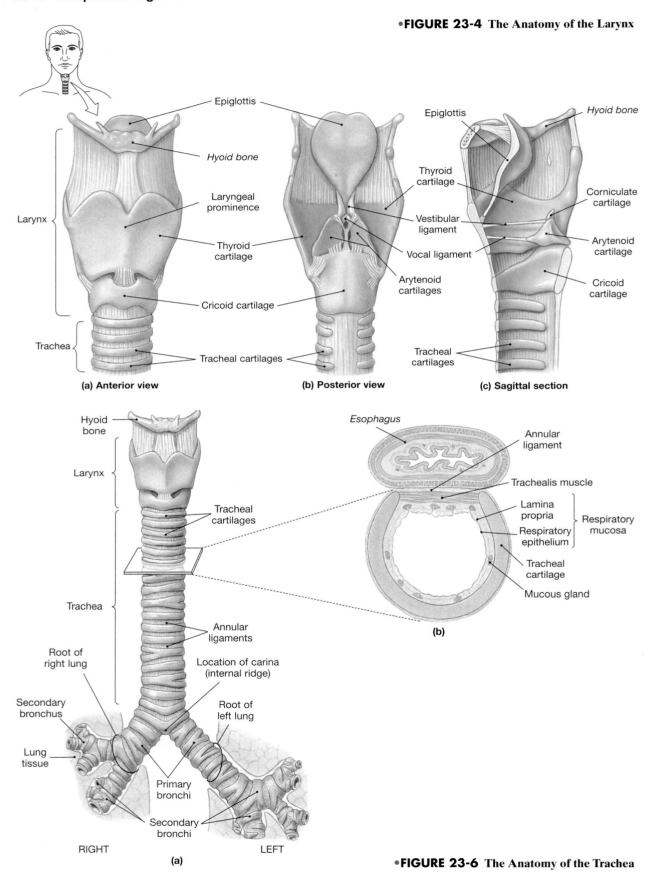

•**FIGURE 23-4** The Anatomy of the Larynx

(a) Anterior view

(b) Posterior view

(c) Sagittal section

(a)

(b)

•**FIGURE 23-6** The Anatomy of the Trachea

NOTES

•**FIGURE 23-10** The Bronchi and Lobules of the Lung

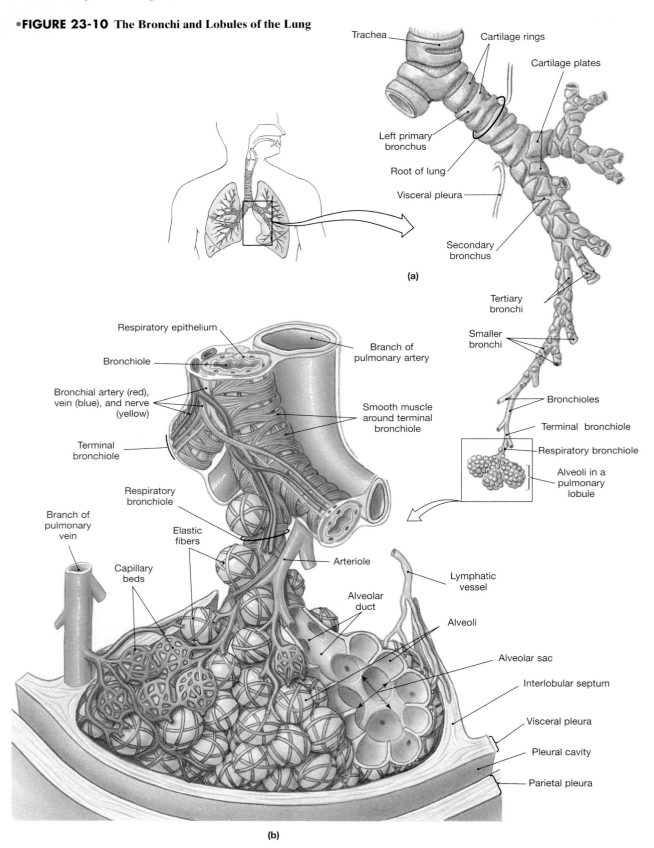

(a)

(b)

NOTES

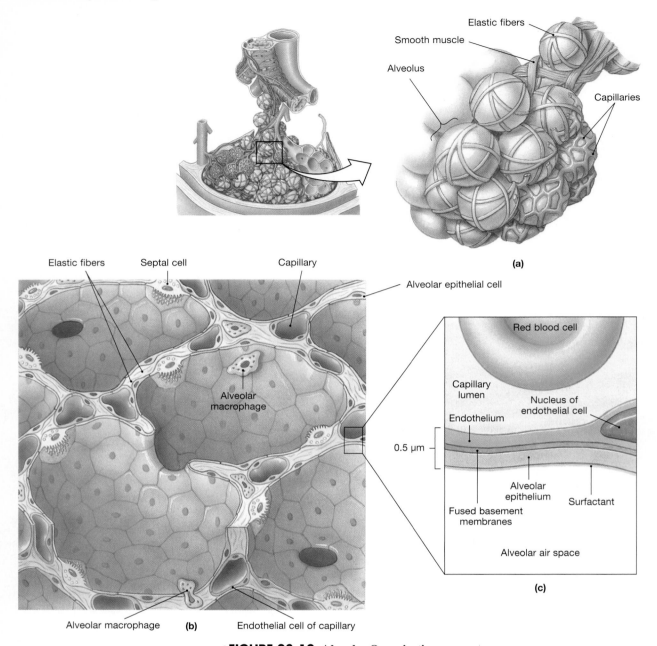

(a)

Elastic fibers   Septal cell   Capillary

Alveolar epithelial cell

Alveolar macrophage

Alveolar macrophage   (b)   Endothelial cell of capillary

Red blood cell

Capillary lumen

Endothelium

Nucleus of endothelial cell

0.5 μm

Alveolar epithelium

Surfactant

Fused basement membranes

Alveolar air space

(c)

•FIGURE 23-12 Alveolar Organization

NOTES

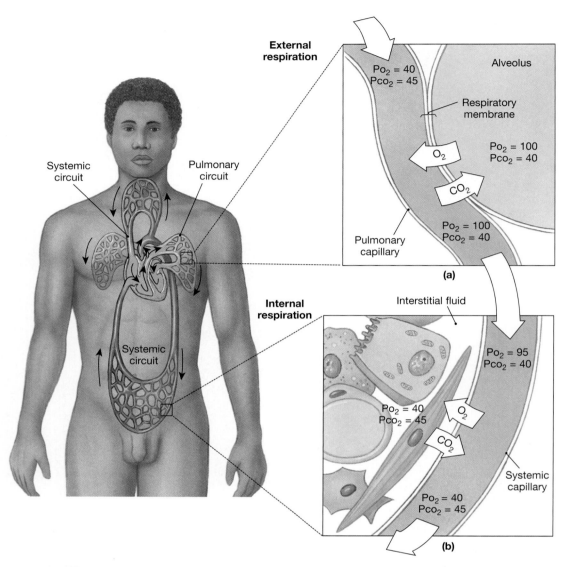

•FIGURE 23-20 An Overview of Respiratory Processes and Partial Pressures in Respiration

NOTES

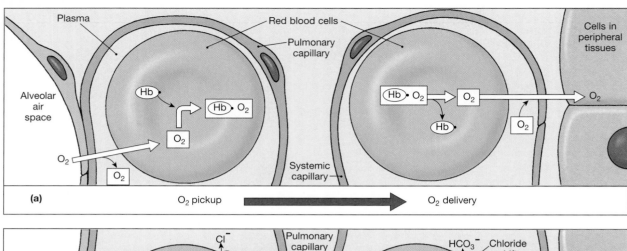

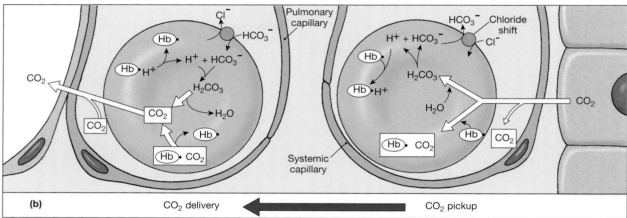

•FIGURE 23-25 A Summary of the Primary Gas Transport Mechanisms

NOTES

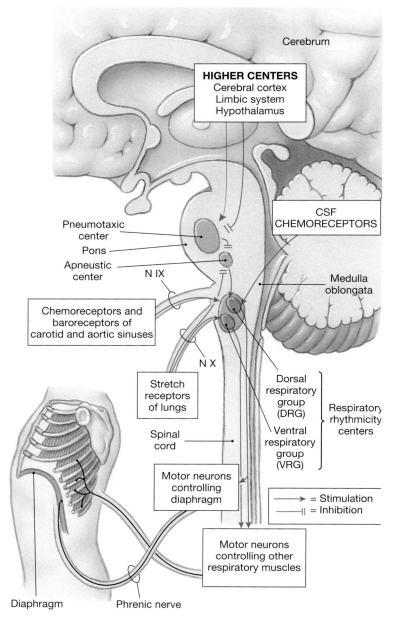

•**FIGURE 23-27** **Respiratory Centers and Reflex Controls**

NOTES

24 The Digestive System

CHAPTER OUTLINE

CHAPTER OBJECTIVES

1. Identify the organs of the digestive system.
2. List the functions of the digestive system.
3. Describe the functional histology of the digestive tract.
4. Describe the processes by which materials move through the digestive tract.
5. Describe the mechanisms that regulate digestion.
6. Describe the anatomy and functions of the oral cavity, pharynx, and esophagus.
7. Describe the anatomy of the stomach, its histological features, and its roles in digestion and absorption.
8. Describe the anatomical and histological characteristics of the small intestine.
9. Explain the functions of the intestinal secretions, and discuss the regulation of secretory activities.
10. Describe the structure, functions, and regulation of the accessory digestive organs.
11. Describe the structure of the large intestine, its movements, and its absorptive processes.
12. Describe the digestion and absorption of organic and inorganic nutrients.
13. Give examples of interactions between the digestive system and each of the other organ systems.

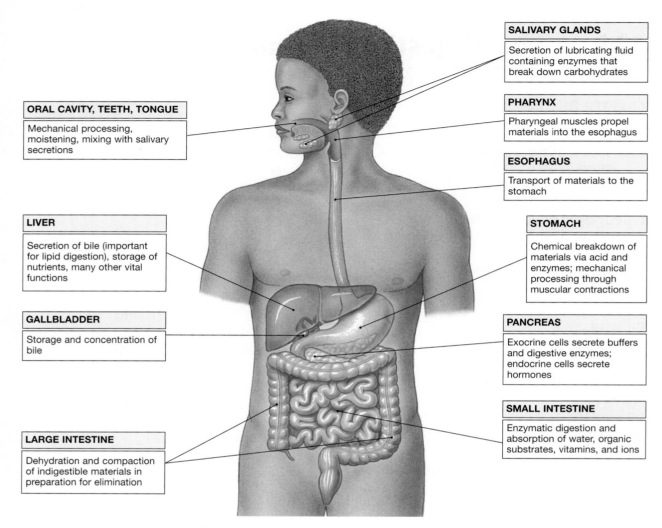

SALIVARY GLANDS

Secretion of lubricating fluid containing enzymes that break down carbohydrates

PHARYNX

Pharyngeal muscles propel materials into the esophagus

ESOPHAGUS

Transport of materials to the stomach

STOMACH

Chemical breakdown of materials via acid and enzymes; mechanical processing through muscular contractions

PANCREAS

Exocrine cells secrete buffers and digestive enzymes; endocrine cells secrete hormones

SMALL INTESTINE

Enzymatic digestion and absorption of water, organic substrates, vitamins, and ions

ORAL CAVITY, TEETH, TONGUE

Mechanical processing, moistening, mixing with salivary secretions

LIVER

Secretion of bile (important for lipid digestion), storage of nutrients, many other vital functions

GALLBLADDER

Storage and concentration of bile

LARGE INTESTINE

Dehydration and compaction of indigestible materials in preparation for elimination

•**FIGURE 24-1** The Components of the Digestive System

NOTES

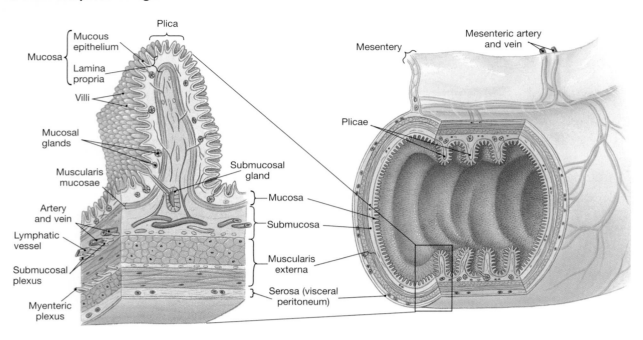

•FIGURE 24-2 The Structure of the Digestive Tract

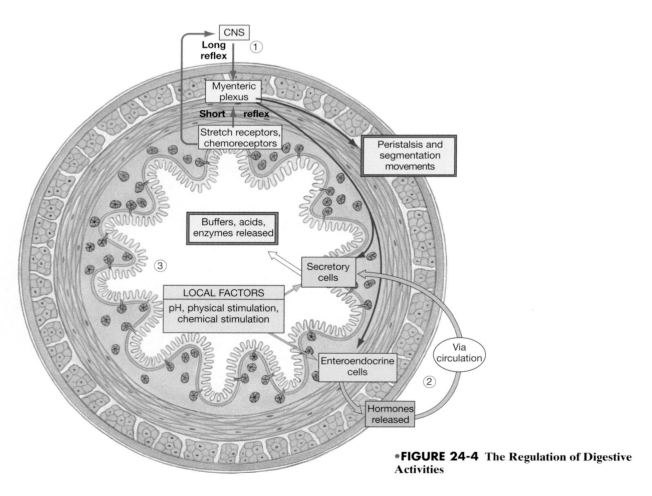

•FIGURE 24-4 The Regulation of Digestive Activities

NOTES
_____

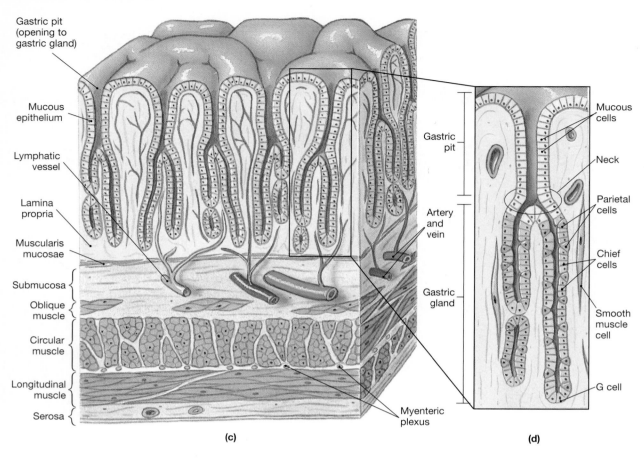

Gastric pit
(opening to
gastric gland)

Mucous
epithelium

Lymphatic
vessel

Lamina
propria

Muscularis
mucosae

Submucosa

Oblique
muscle

Circular
muscle

Longitudinal
muscle

Serosa

Artery
and
vein

Myenteric
plexus

(c)

Gastric
pit

Gastric
gland

Mucous
cells

Neck

Parietal
cells

Chief
cells

Smooth
muscle
cell

G cell

(d)

•**FIGURE 24-13** **The Stomach Lining**

NOTES

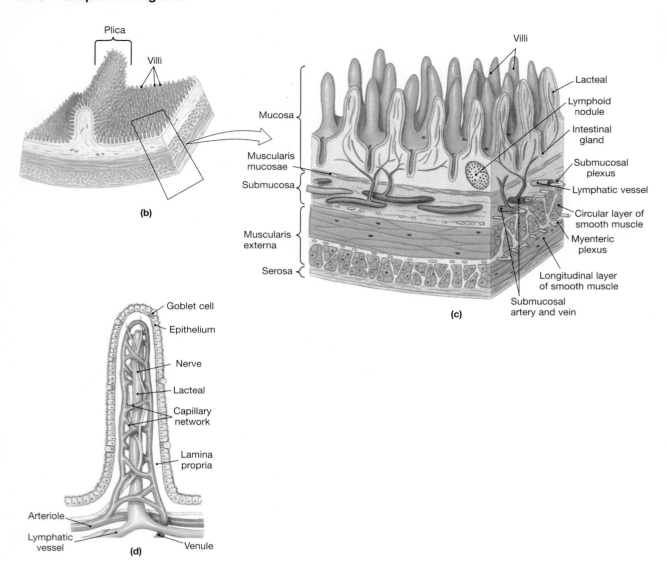

•FIGURE 24-17 The Intestinal Wall

NOTES

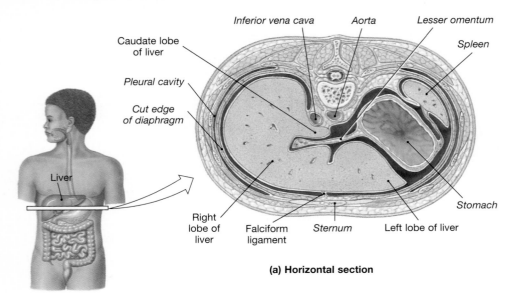

Inferior vena cava   Aorta   Lesser omentum

Caudate lobe
of liver

Spleen

Pleural cavity

Cut edge
of diaphragm

Liver

Right
lobe of
liver

Falciform
ligament

Sternum

Left lobe of liver

Stomach

(a) Horizontal section

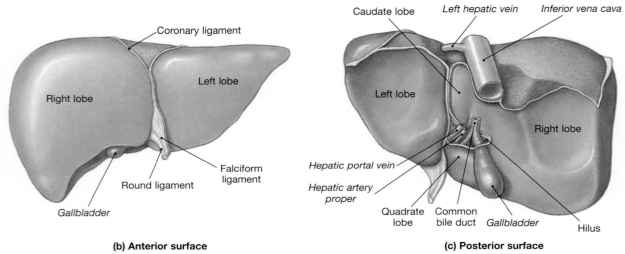

Coronary ligament

Right lobe

Left lobe

Gallbladder

Round ligament

Falciform
ligament

(b) Anterior surface

Caudate lobe   Left hepatic vein   Inferior vena cava

Left lobe

Right lobe

Hepatic portal vein

Hepatic artery
proper

Quadrate
lobe

Common
bile duct

Gallbladder

Hilus

(c) Posterior surface

•**FIGURE 24-19** The Anatomy of the Liver

NOTES
_____

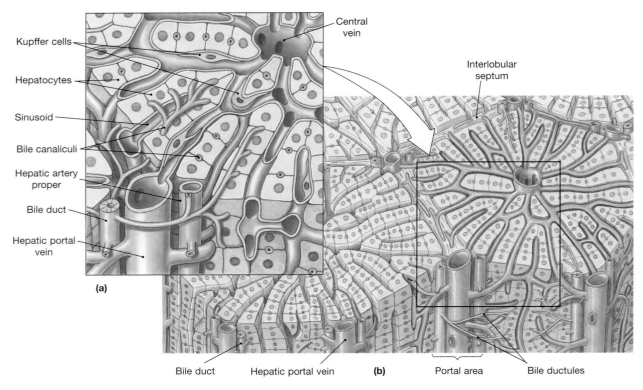

Kupffer cells

Hepatocytes

Sinusoid

Bile canaliculi

Hepatic artery proper

Bile duct

Hepatic portal vein

Central vein

Interlobular septum

(a)

Bile duct   Hepatic portal vein   (b)   Portal area   Bile ductules

•**FIGURE 24-20** Liver Histology

NOTES

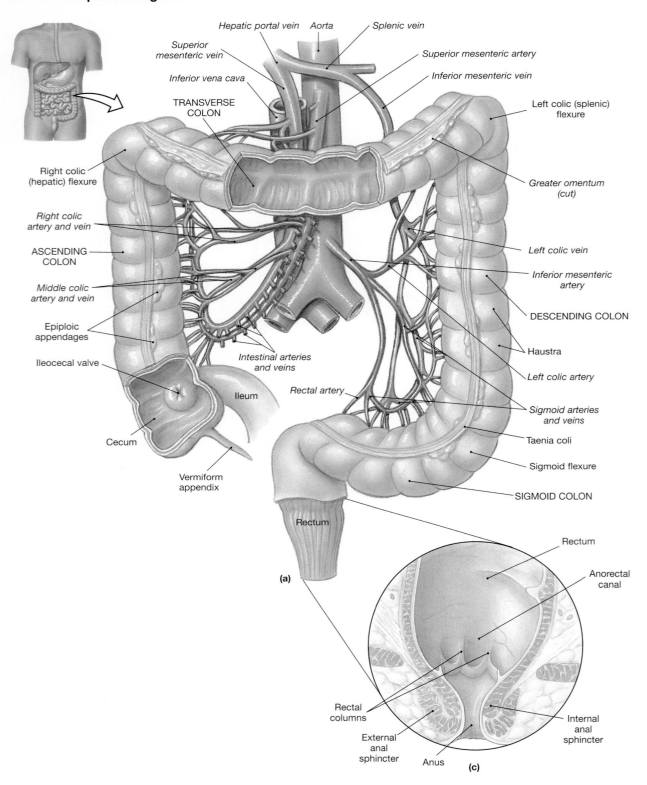

Hepatic portal vein
Aorta
Splenic vein
Superior mesenteric vein
Superior mesenteric artery
Inferior vena cava
Inferior mesenteric vein
TRANSVERSE COLON
Left colic (splenic) flexure
Right colic (hepatic) flexure
Greater omentum (cut)
Right colic artery and vein
Left colic vein
ASCENDING COLON
Inferior mesenteric artery
Middle colic artery and vein
DESCENDING COLON
Epiploic appendages
Haustra
Left colic artery
Intestinal arteries and veins
Ileocecal valve
Rectal artery
Sigmoid arteries and veins
Ileum
Taenia coli
Cecum
Sigmoid flexure
SIGMOID COLON
Vermiform appendix
Rectum
(a)

Rectum
Anorectal canal
Rectal columns
External anal sphincter
Internal anal sphincter
Anus
(c)

•FIGURE 24-23 The Large Intestine

© 2002 Prentice Hall, Inc.

NOTES

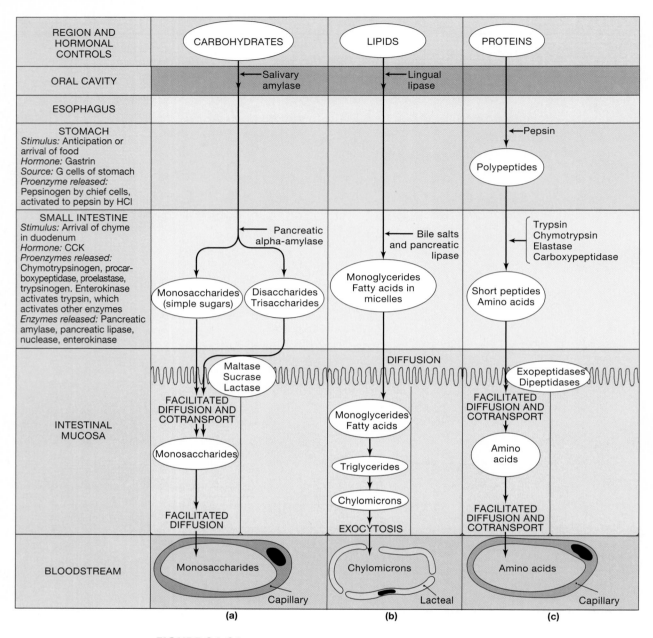

•FIGURE 24-26 A Summary of the Chemical Events in Digestion

NOTES

25   Metabolism and Energetics

CHAPTER OUTLINE

CHAPTER OBJECTIVES

1. Define *metabolism*, and explain why cells need to synthesize new organic components.
2. Describe the basic steps in glycolysis, the TCA cycle, and the electron transport chain.
3. Summarize the energy yield of glycolysis and cellular respiration.
4. Describe the pathways involved in lipid metabolism and the mechanisms necessary for lipid transport and distribution.
5. Discuss protein metabolism and the use of proteins as an energy source.
6. Discuss nucleic acid metabolism.
7. Differentiate between the absorptive and postabsorptive metabolic states, and summarize the characteristics of each.
8. Explain what constitutes a balanced diet and why such a diet is important.
9. Define *metabolic rate*, and discuss the factors involved in determining an individual's BMR.
10. Discuss the homeostatic mechanisms that maintain a constant body temperature.

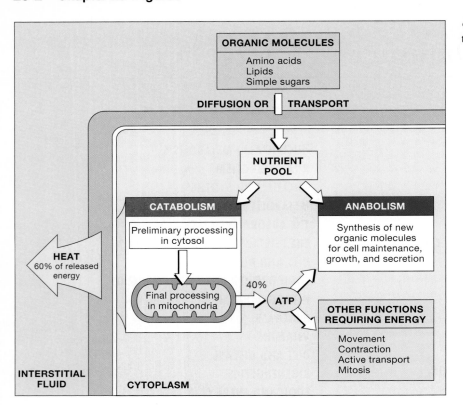

•FIGURE 25-1 An Introduction to Cellular Metabolism

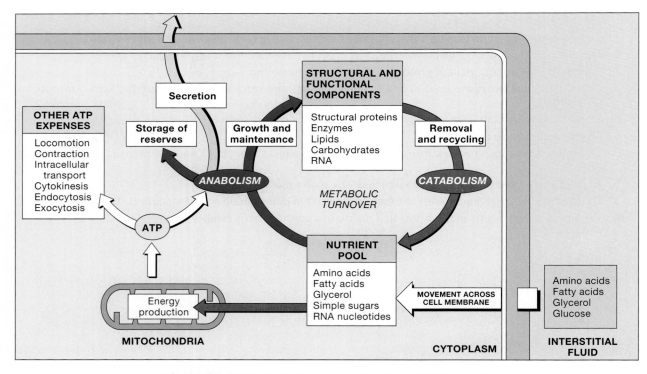

•FIGURE 25-2 Metabolic Turnover and Cellular ATP Production

NOTES

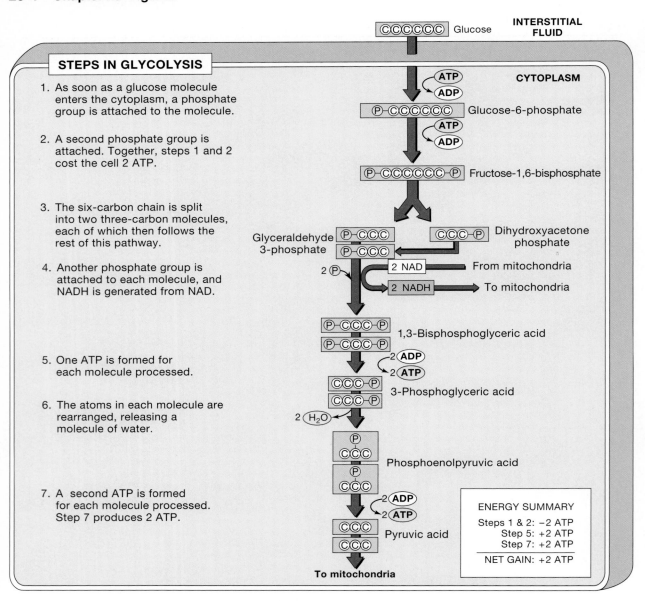

•FIGURE 25-4 Glycolysis

NOTES

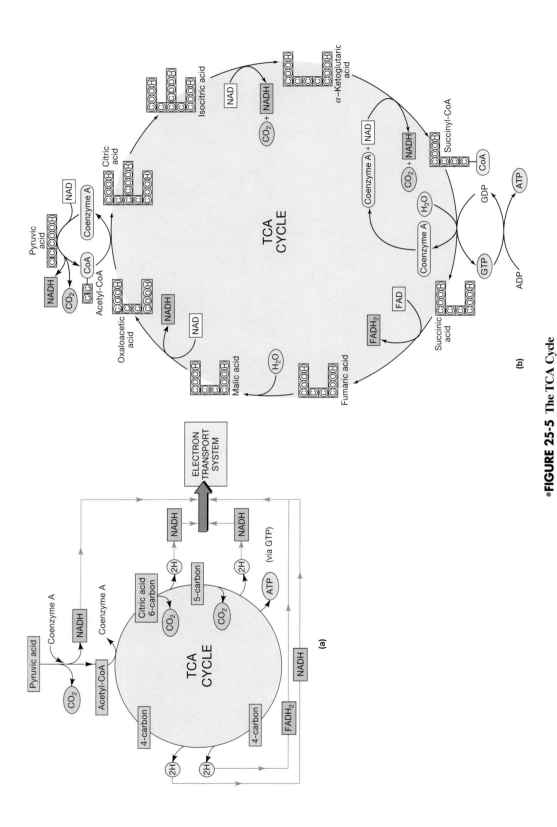

•**FIGURE 25-5** The TCA Cycle

NOTES

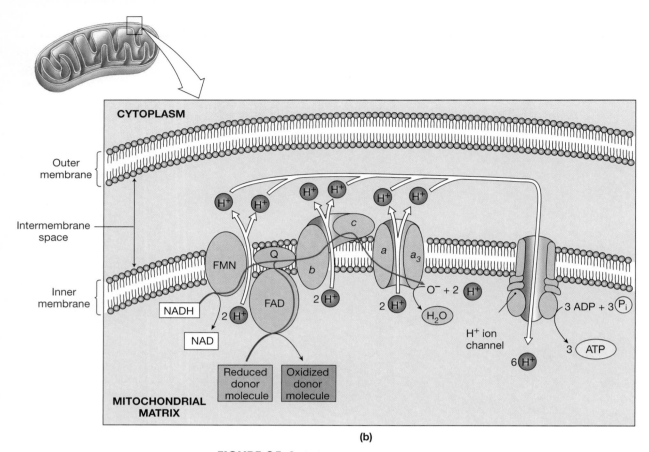

(b)

•**FIGURE 25-6** Oxidative Phosphorylation

NOTES

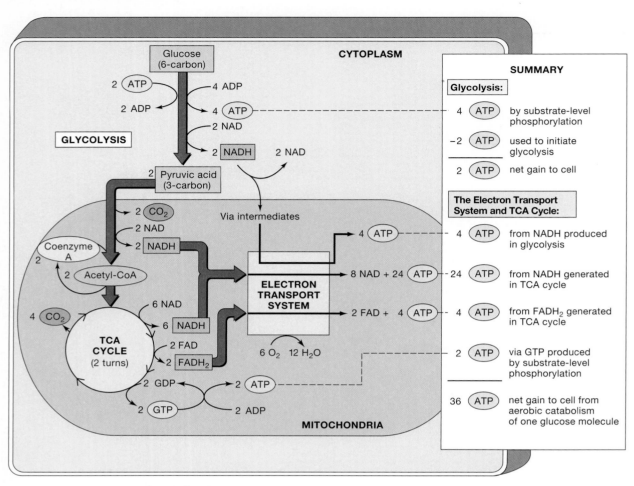

•**FIGURE 25-7** A Summary of the Energy Yield of Aerobic Metabolism

NOTES

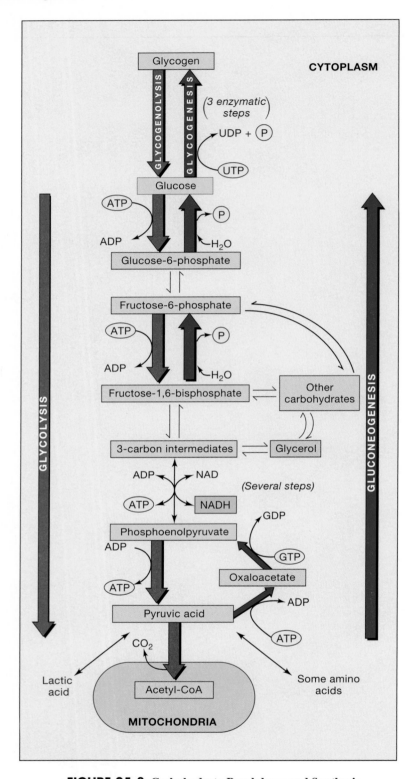

•**FIGURE 25-8** Carbohydrate Breakdown and Synthesis

NOTES

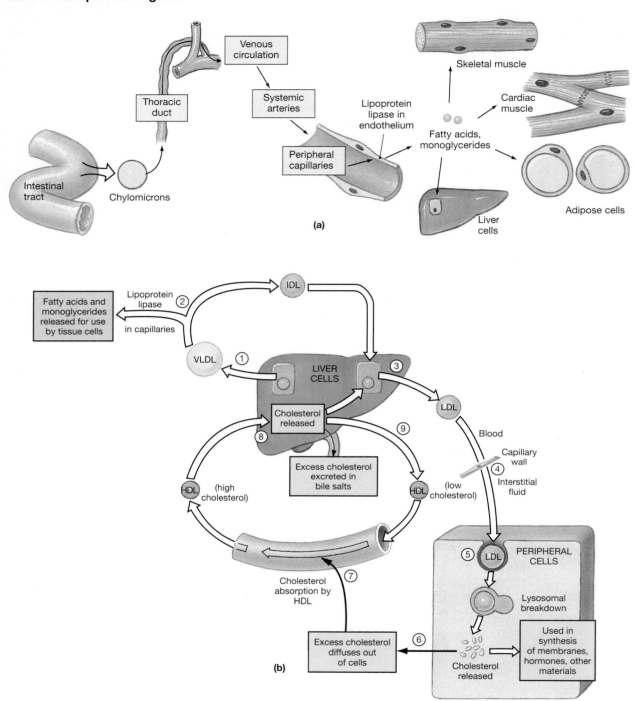

•FIGURE 25-11 Lipid Transport and Utilization

NOTES

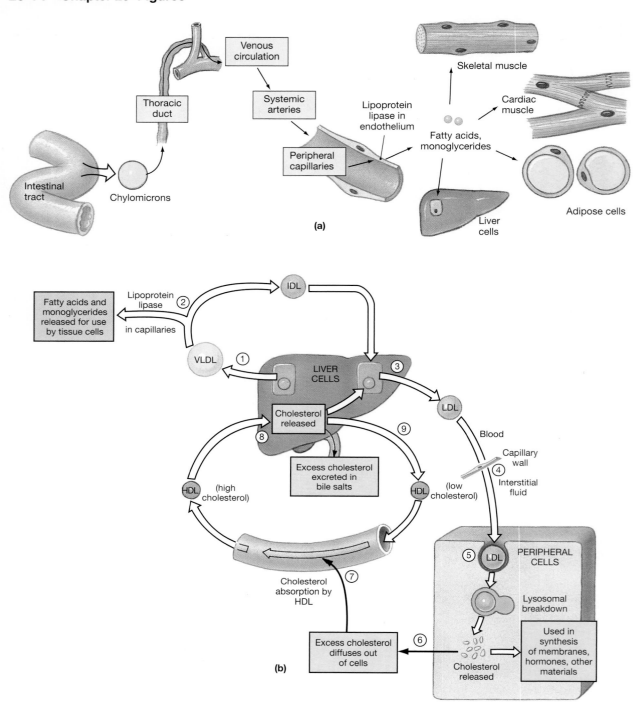

•FIGURE 25-11 Lipid Transport and Utilization

NOTES

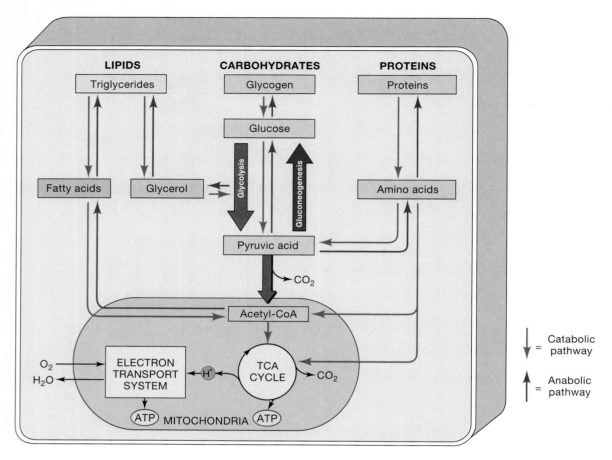

•**FIGURE 25-14** A Summary of the Pathways of Catabolism and Anabolism

NOTES

26   The Urinary System

CHAPTER OUTLINE

CHAPTER OBJECTIVES

1. Identify the components of the urinary system, and describe the vital functions performed by this system.
2. Describe the structural features of the kidneys.
3. Describe the structure of the nephron and the processes involved in the formation of urine.
4. Identify the major blood vessels associated with each kidney, and trace the path of blood flow through a kidney.
5. List and describe the factors that influence filtration pressure and the rate of filtrate formation.
6. Identify the types of transport mechanisms found along the nephron, and discuss the reabsorptive or secretory functions of each segment of the nephron and collecting system.
7. Explain the role of countercurrent multiplication in the formation of a concentration gradient in the renal medulla.
8. Describe how antidiuretic hormone and aldosterone levels influence the volume and concentration of urine.
9. Describe the normal characteristics, composition, and solute concentrations of a representative urine sample.
10. Describe the structures and functions of the ureters, urinary bladder, and urethra.
11. Discuss the voluntary and involuntary regulation of urination, and describe the micturition reflex.
12. Describe the effects of aging on the urinary system.
13. Give examples of interactions between the urinary system and each of the other organ systems.

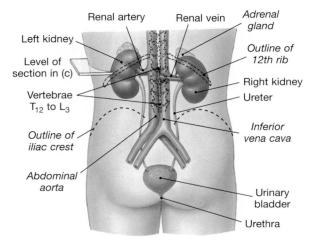

Renal artery   Renal vein   *Adrenal gland*

Left kidney

Outline of 12th rib

Level of section in (c)

Right kidney

Vertebrae T$_{12}$ to L$_3$

Ureter

Outline of iliac crest

Inferior vena cava

Abdominal aorta

Urinary bladder

Urethra

(a) Posterior view

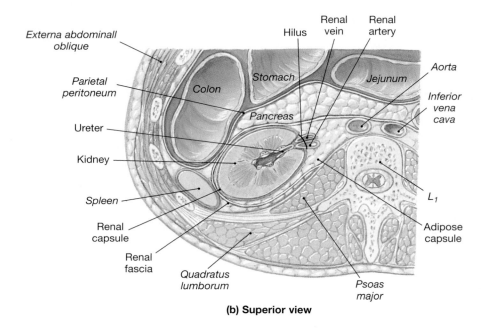

Externa abdominall oblique

Hilus

Renal vein

Renal artery

Parietal peritoneum

Stomach

Colon

Jejunum

Aorta

Pancreas

Inferior vena cava

Ureter

Kidney

Spleen

L$_1$

Renal capsule

Renal fascia

Adipose capsule

Quadratus lumborum

Psoas major

(b) Superior view

•**FIGURE 26-2** The Position of the Kidneys

NOTES

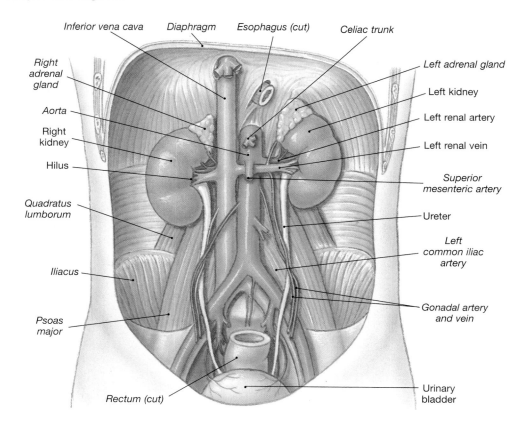

•**FIGURE 26-3** The Urinary System in Gross Dissection

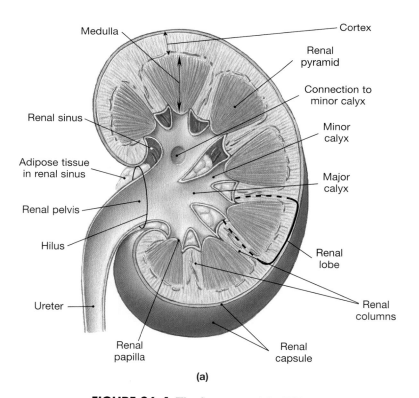

(a)

•**FIGURE 26-4** The Structure of the Kidney

NOTES

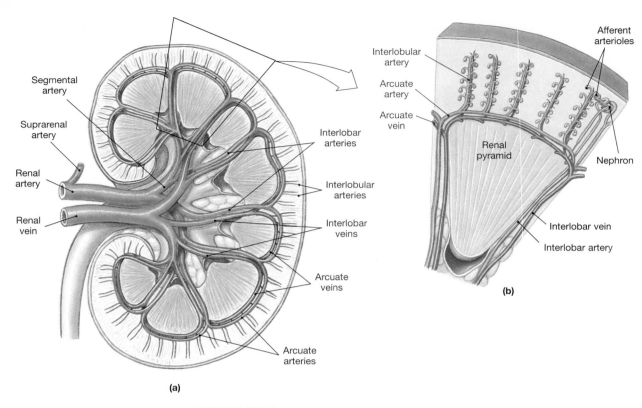

Segmental artery

Suprarenal artery

Renal artery

Renal vein

Interlobar arteries

Interlobular arteries

Interlobar veins

Arcuate veins

Arcuate arteries

(a)

Interlobular artery

Arcuate artery

Arcuate vein

Renal pyramid

Afferent arterioles

Nephron

Interlobar vein

Interlobar artery

(b)

•FIGURE 26-5 The Blood Supply to the Kidneys

NOTES

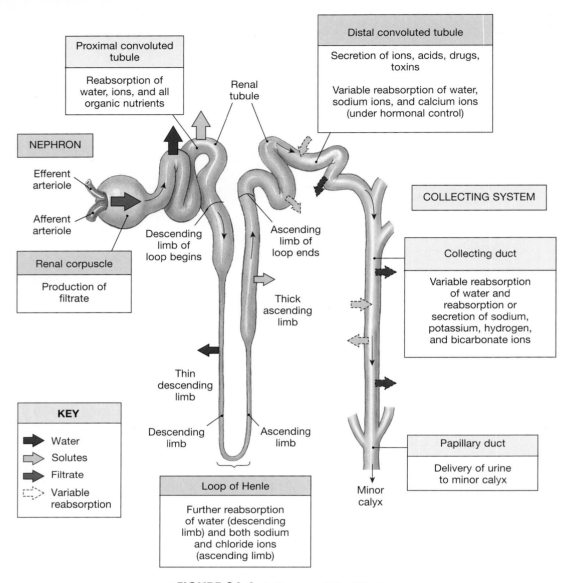

•**FIGURE 26-6** A Representative Nephron

NOTES

TABLE 26-1 The Organization of the Nephron and Collecting System in the Kidney

Region	Length	Diameter	Primary Function	Histological Characteristics
NEPHRON				
Renal corpuscle	150–250 μm (spherical)	150–250 μm	Filtration of plasma	Glomerulus (capillary knot), supporting cells, and lamina densa, enclosed by Bowman's capsule; visceral epithelium (podocytes) and parietal epithelium separated by capsular space
Renal tubule				
Proximal convoluted tubule (PCT)	14 mm	60 μm	Reabsorption of ions, organic molecules, vitamins, water; secretion of drugs, toxins, acids	Cuboidal cells with microvilli
Loop of Henle, Thin segment	30 mm	15 μm	Descending limb: reabsorption of water from tubular fluid	Squamous or low cuboidal cells
Thick segment		30 μm	Ascending limb: reabsorption of ions; assists in creation of a concentration gradient in the medulla	
Distal convoluted tubule (DCT)	5 mm	30–50 μm	Reabsorption of sodium ions and calcium ions; secretion of acids, ammonia, drugs, toxins	Cuboidal cells with few if any microvilli
COLLECTING SYSTEM				
Collecting duct	15 mm	50–100 μm	Reabsorption of water, sodium ions; secretion or reabsorption of bicarbonate ions or hydrogen ions	Cuboidal to columnar cells
Papillary duct	5 mm	100–200 μm	Conduction of tubular fluid to minor calyx; contributes to concentration gradient of the medulla	Columnar cells

NOTES

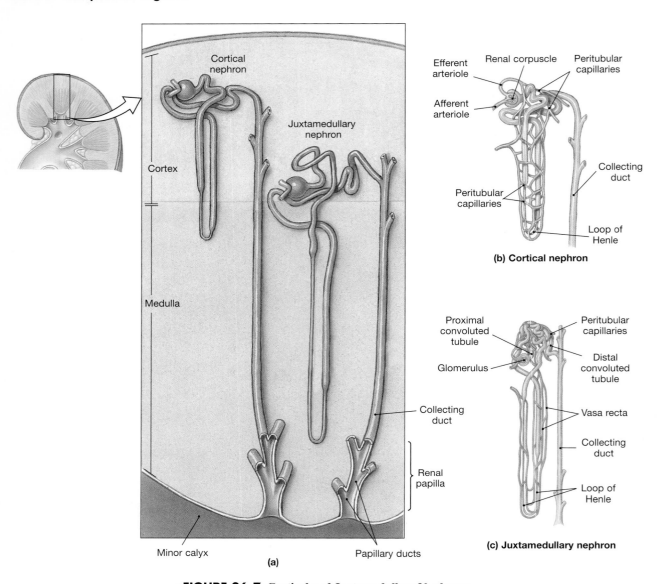

•**FIGURE 26-7** **Cortical and Juxtamedullary Nephrons**

NOTES

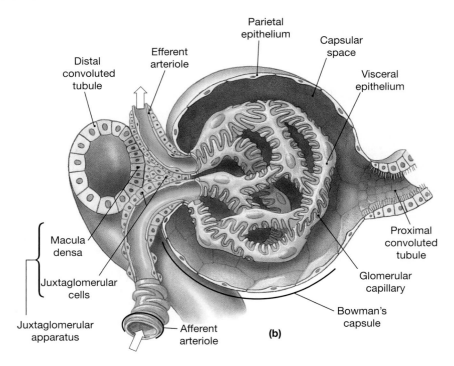

(b)

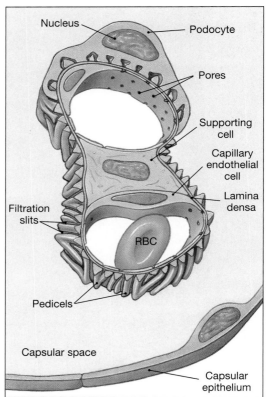

(d)

•FIGURE 26-8 The Renal Corpuscle

NOTES

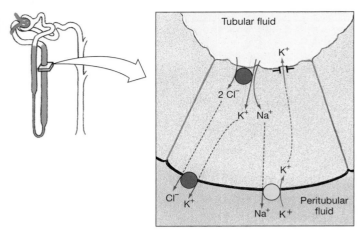

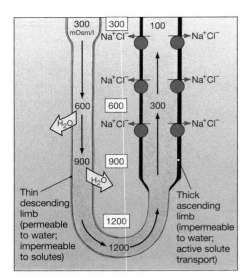

(a) The mechanism of sodium and chloride ion transport involves (1) a $Na^+–K^+/$ $2 Cl^-$ carrier at the apical surface and (2) two carriers at the basal surface of the tubular cell: a potassium–chloride cotransport pump and a sodium–potassium exchange pump. Because the potassium ions removed from the lumen of the tubule ultimately diffuse back in through leak channels, the net result is the transport of sodium and chloride ions into the peritubular fluid.

(b) Active transport of NaCl along the ascending thick limb results in the movement of water from the descending limb.

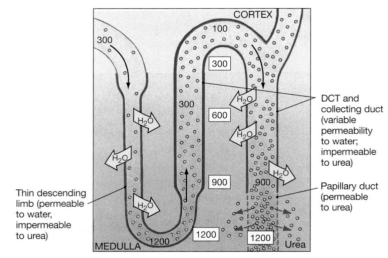

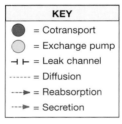

KEY	
●	= Cotransport
○	= Exchange pump
⊣ ⊢	= Leak channel
-------	= Diffusion
---▶	= Reabsorption
---▶	= Secretion

(c) The permeability characteristics of both the loop and the collecting duct tend to concentrate urea in the tubular fluid and in the medulla. The loop of Henle, DCT, and collecting duct are impermeable to urea. As water reabsorption occurs, the urea concentration rises. The papillary ducts' permeability to urea accounts for roughly one-third of the solutes in the deepest portions of the medulla.

•**FIGURE 26-12** **Countercurrent Multiplication and Concentration of Urine**

NOTES

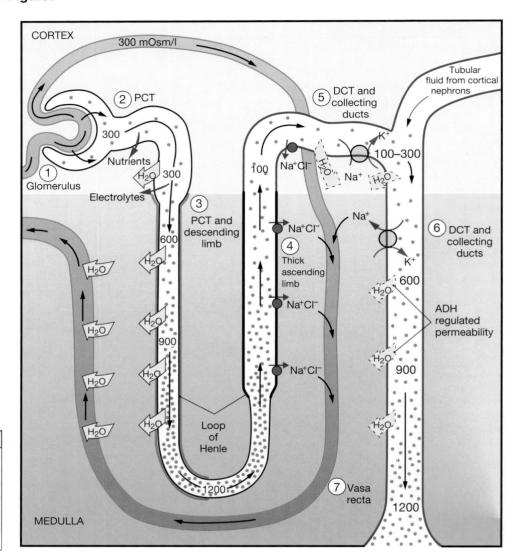

KEY

● = Cotransport
○ = Exchange pump
⊣ ⊢ = Leak channel
- - - - - = Diffusion
- - - ▶ = Reabsorption
- - - ▶ = Secretion

•**FIGURE 26-15** A Summary of Renal Function

NOTES

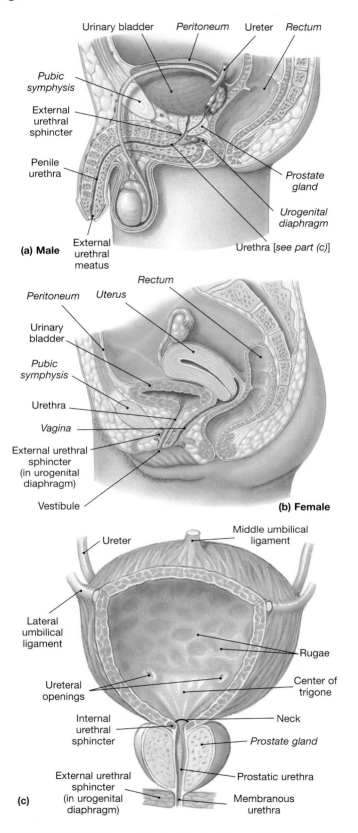

Urinary bladder   Peritoneum   Ureter   Rectum

Pubic symphysis

External urethral sphincter

Penile urethra

Prostate gland

Urogenital diaphragm

Urethra [see part (c)]

(a) Male   External urethral meatus

Rectum

Peritoneum   Uterus

Urinary bladder

Pubic symphysis

Urethra

Vagina

External urethral sphincter (in urogenital diaphragm)

Vestibule

(b) Female

Ureter   Middle umbilical ligament

Lateral umbilical ligament

Rugae

Ureteral openings

Center of trigone

Internal urethral sphincter

Neck

Prostate gland

External urethral sphincter (in urogenital diaphragm)

Prostatic urethra

Membranous urethra

(c)

•FIGURE 26-18 Organs for the Conduction and Storage of Urine

NOTES

CHAPTER

27 Fluid, Electrolyte, and Acid–Base Balance

CHAPTER OUTLINE

CHAPTER OBJECTIVES

1. Compare the composition of intracellular and extracellular fluids.
2. Explain the basic concepts involved in the regulation of fluids and electrolytes.
3. Identify the hormones that play important roles in regulating fluid balance and electrolyte balance, and describe their effects.
4. Discuss the mechanisms by which sodium, potassium, calcium, and chloride ion concentrations are regulated to maintain electrolyte balance.
5. Explain the buffering systems that balance the pH of the intracellular and extracellular fluids.
6. Describe the compensatory mechanisms involved in the maintenance of acid–base balance.
7. Identify the most frequent threats to acid–base balance, and explain how the body responds when the pH of body fluids varies outside normal limits.

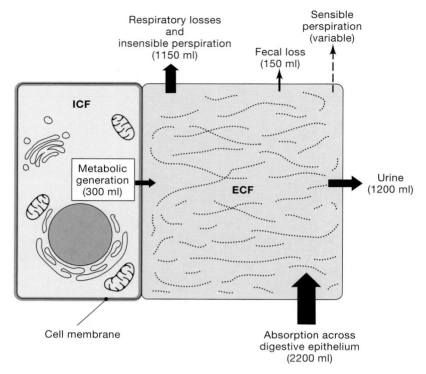

•**FIGURE 27-3** Fluid Exchanges

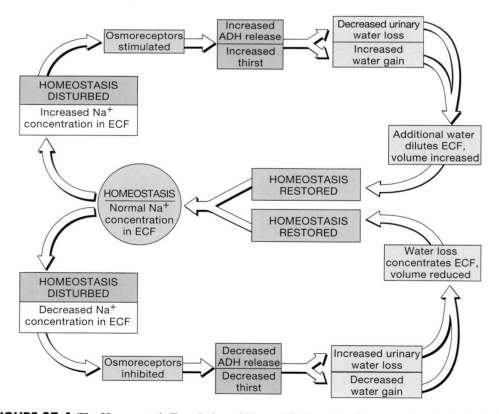

•**FIGURE 27-4** The Homeostatic Regulation of Normal Sodium Ion Concentrations in Body Fluids

NOTES

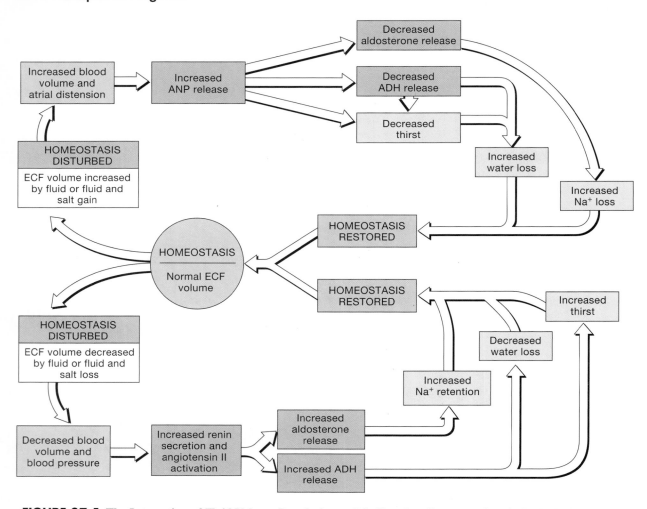

•**FIGURE 27-5** The Integration of Fluid Volume Regulation and Sodium Ion Concentrations in Body Fluids

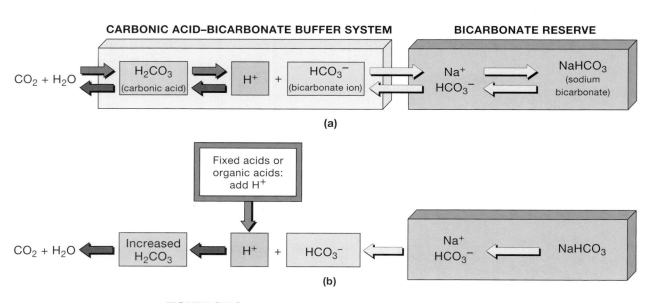

•**FIGURE 27-9** The Carbonic Acid–Bicarbonate Buffer System

© 2002 Prentice Hall, Inc.

NOTES

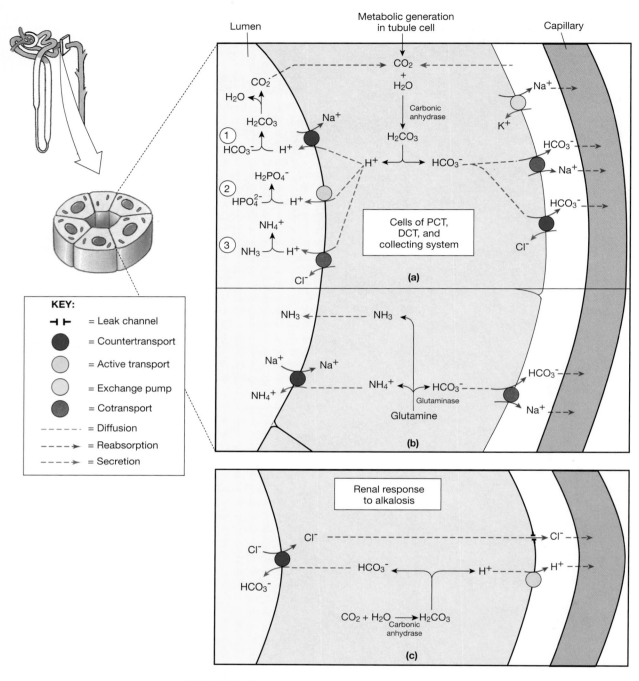

•FIGURE 27-10 Kidney Tubules and pH Regulation

NOTES

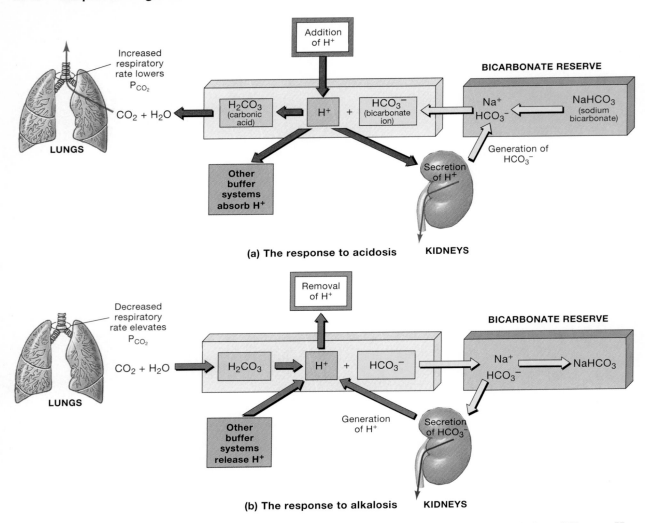

(a) The response to acidosis

(b) The response to alkalosis

•**FIGURE 27-11** The Central Role of the Carbonic Acid–Bicarbonate Buffer System in the Regulation of Plasma pH

NOTES

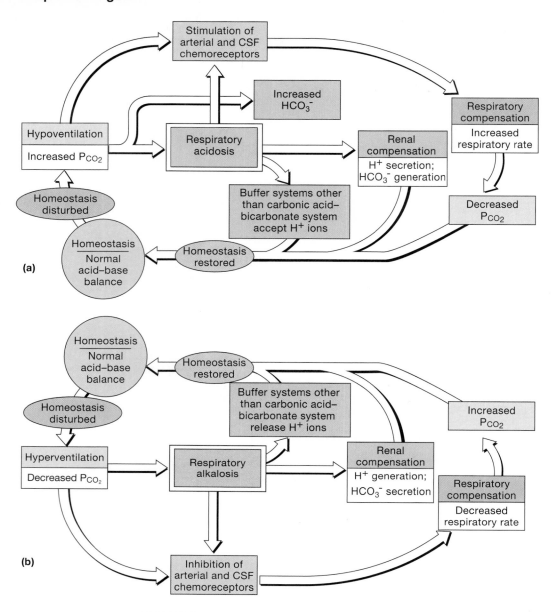

•FIGURE 27-12 Respiratory Acid–Base Regulation

NOTES
_____

28   The Reproductive System

CHAPTER OUTLINE

CHAPTER OBJECTIVES

1. Summarize the functions of the human reproductive system and its principal components.
2. Describe the components of the male reproductive system.
3. Discuss the processes of meiosis and spermatogenesis in the testes.
4. Describe the roles the male reproductive tract and accessory glands play in the functional maturation, nourishment, storage, and transport of spermatozoa.
5. Discuss the normal composition of semen.
6. Describe the male external genitalia.
7. Describe the hormonal mechanisms that regulate male reproductive functions.
8. Describe the components of the female reproductive system.
9. Discuss the processes of meiosis and oogenesis in the ovaries.
10. Identify the phases and events of the ovarian and uterine cycles.
11. Describe the structure, histology, and functions of the vagina.
12. Name and describe the parts of the female external genitalia and mammary glands.
13. Describe the anatomical, physiological, and hormonal aspects of the female reproductive cycle.
14. Discuss the physiology of sexual intercourse as it affects the reproductive systems of males and females.
15. Describe the changes in the reproductive system that occur with aging.
16. Give examples of interactions between the reproductive system and each of the other organ systems.

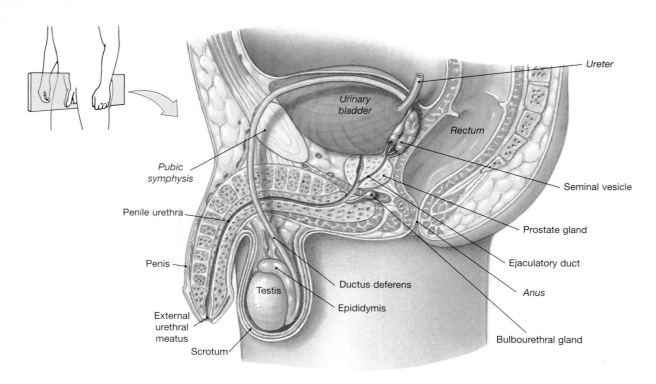

●**FIGURE 28-1** The Male Reproductive System

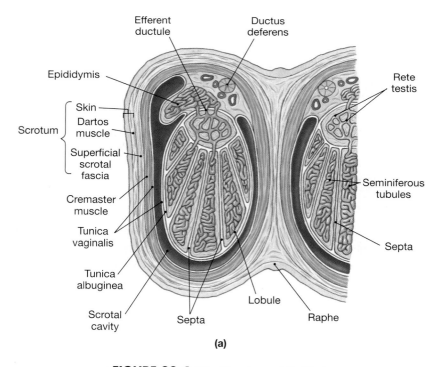

(a)

●**FIGURE 28-4** The Structure of the Testes

NOTES

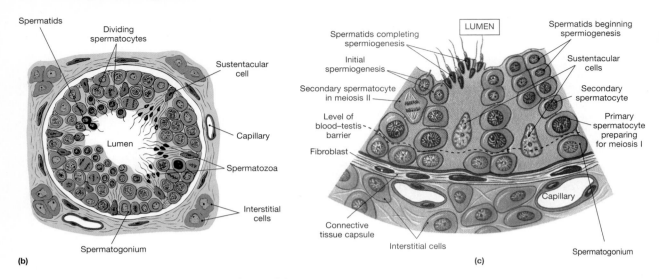

•**FIGURE 28-5** The Seminiferous Tubules

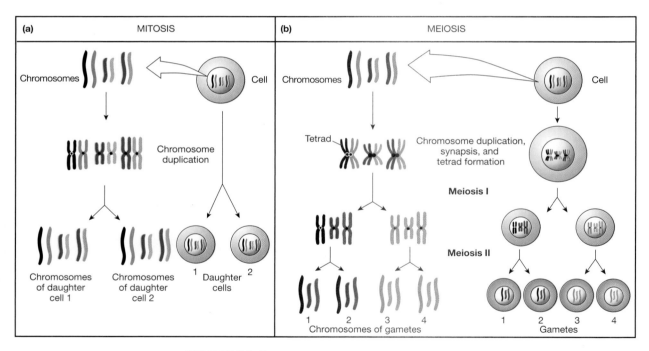

•**FIGURE 28-6** Chromosomes in Mitosis and Meiosis

NOTES

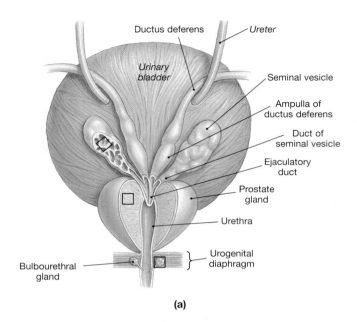

(a)

•**FIGURE 28-10** The Ductus Deferens and Accessory Glands

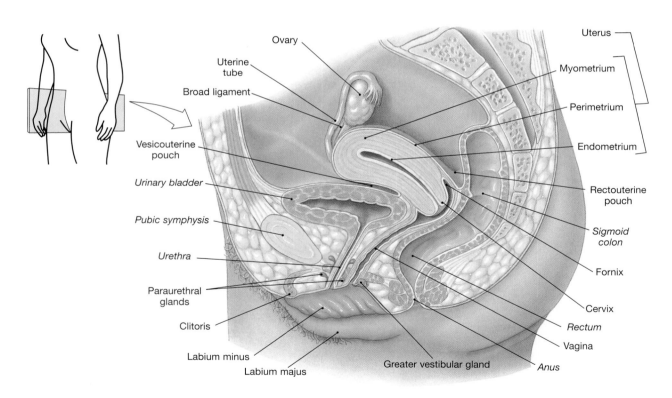

•**FIGURE 28-13** The Female Reproductive System

NOTES

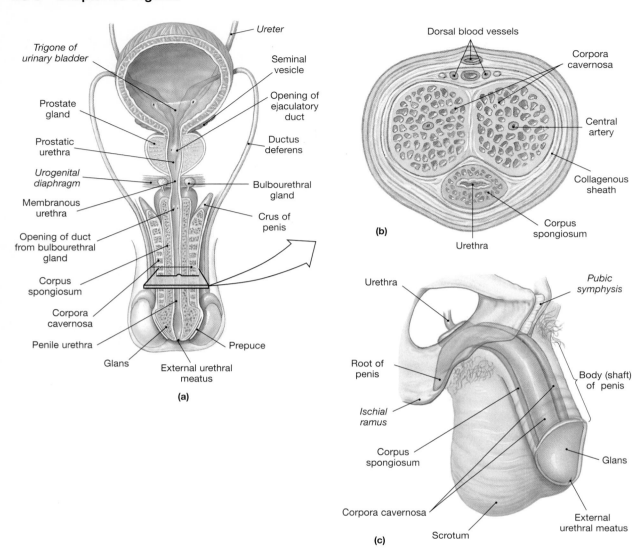

(a)

(b)

(c)

•**FIGURE 28-11** **The Penis**

NOTES

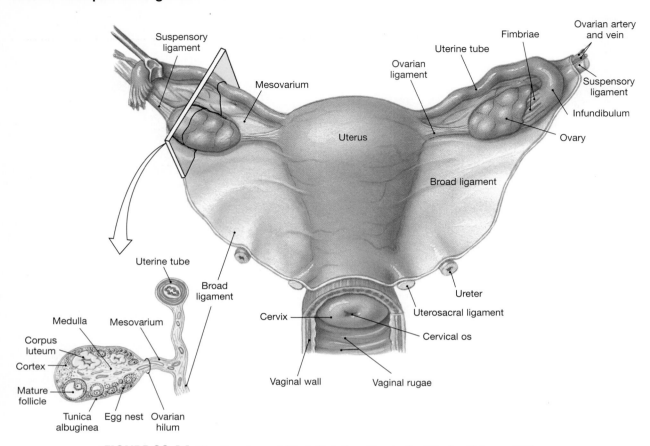

•**FIGURE 28-14** The Ovaries and Their Relationships to the Uterine Tube and Uterus

NOTES

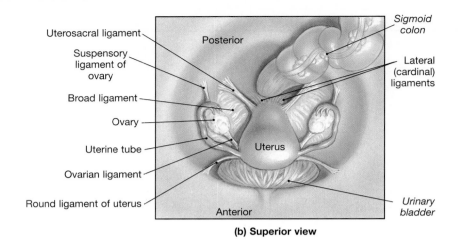

Uterosacral ligament

Suspensory ligament of ovary

Broad ligament

Ovary

Uterine tube

Ovarian ligament

Round ligament of uterus

Posterior

Sigmoid colon

Lateral (cardinal) ligaments

Uterus

Urinary bladder

Anterior

(b) Superior view

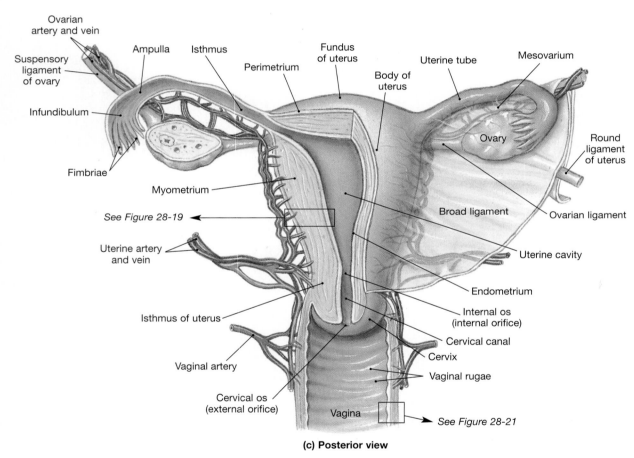

Ovarian artery and vein

Suspensory ligament of ovary

Infundibulum

Fimbriae

Myometrium

See Figure 28-19

Uterine artery and vein

Isthmus of uterus

Vaginal artery

Cervical os (external orifice)

Ampulla

Isthmus

Perimetrium

Fundus of uterus

Body of uterus

Uterine tube

Mesovarium

Ovary

Round ligament of uterus

Broad ligament

Ovarian ligament

Uterine cavity

Endometrium

Internal os (internal orifice)

Cervical canal

Cervix

Vaginal rugae

Vagina

See Figure 28-21

(c) Posterior view

•**FIGURE 28-18** **The Uterus**

© 2002 Prentice Hall, Inc.

NOTES

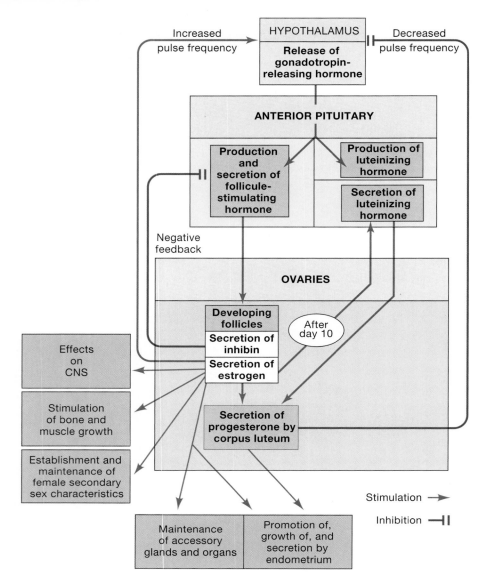

•**FIGURE 28-25** The Hormonal Regulation of Ovarian Activity

NOTES

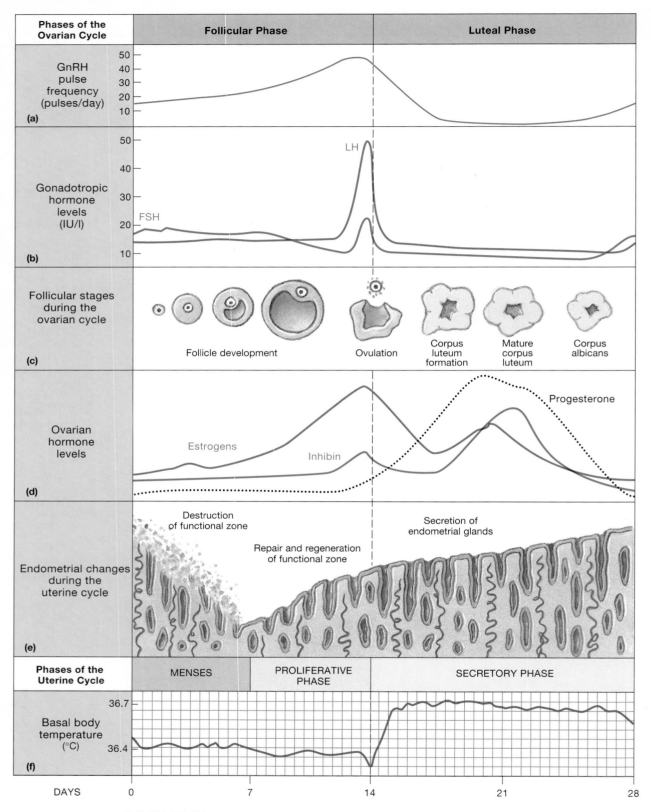

•FIGURE 28-26 The Hormonal Regulation of the Female Reproductive Cycle

NOTES

29   Development and Inheritance

CHAPTER OUTLINE

CHAPTER OBJECTIVES

1. Describe the process of fertilization.
2. Explain how developmental processes are regulated.
3. List the three prenatal periods, and describe the major events associated with each.
4. Explain how the germ layers participate in the formation of extraembryonic membranes.
5. Discuss the importance of the placenta as an endocrine organ.
6. Describe the interplay between the maternal organ systems and the developing fetus.
7. Discuss the structural and functional changes in the uterus during gestation.
8. List and discuss the events that occur during labor and delivery.
9. Identify the features and functions associated with the various life stages.
10. Relate basic principles of genetics to the inheritance of human traits.

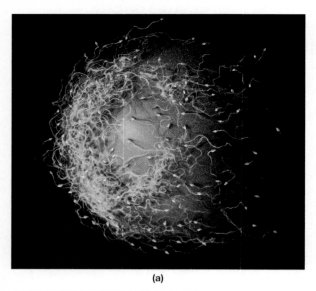

(a)

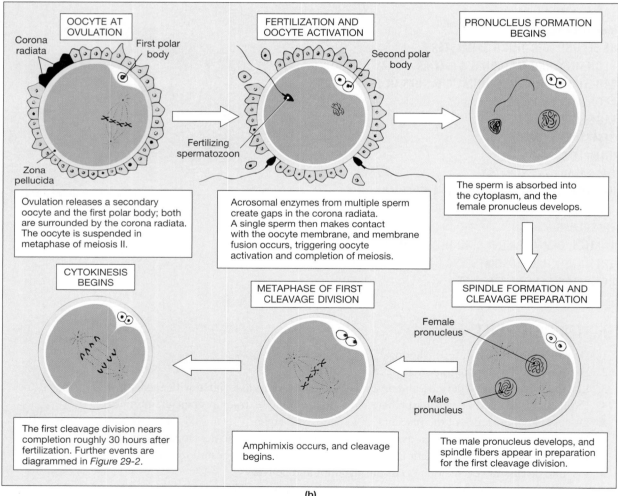

(b)

•FIGURE 29-1 Fertilization

NOTES

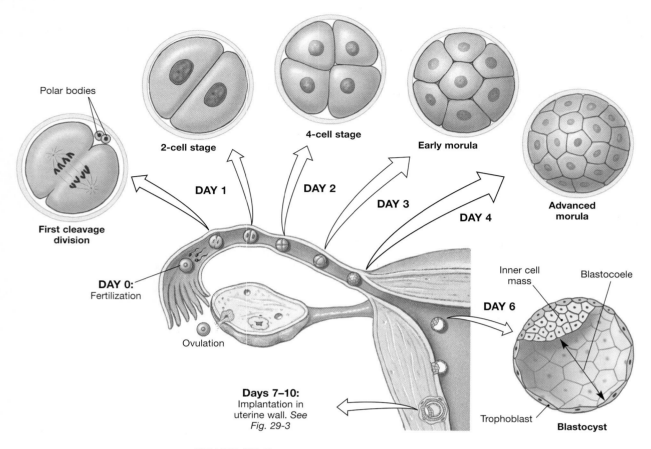

•FIGURE 29-2 Cleavage and Blastocyst Formation

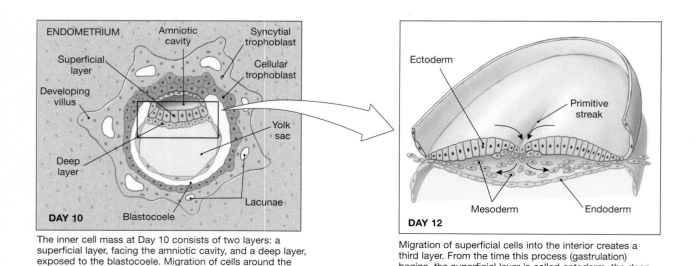

The inner cell mass at Day 10 consists of two layers: a superficial layer, facing the amniotic cavity, and a deep layer, exposed to the blastocoele. Migration of cells around the amniotic cavity is the first step in the formation of the amnion. Migration of cells around the edges of the blastocoele is the first step in yolk sac formation.

Migration of superficial cells into the interior creates a third layer. From the time this process (gastrulation) begins, the superficial layer is called *ectoderm*, the deep layer *endoderm*, and the migrating cells *mesoderm*.

•FIGURE 29-4 The Inner Cell Mass and Gastrulation

© 2002 Prentice Hall, Inc.

NOTES

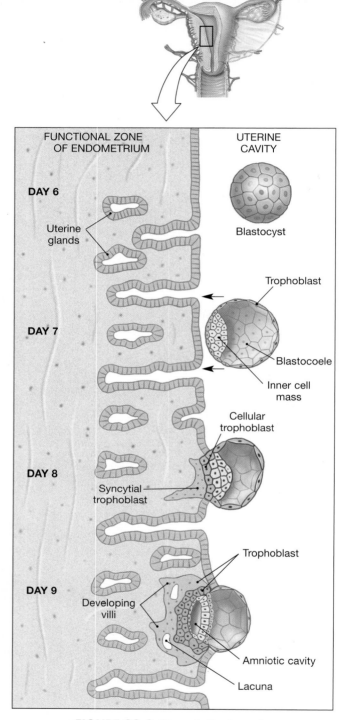

•FIGURE 29-3 Stages in Implantation

NOTES

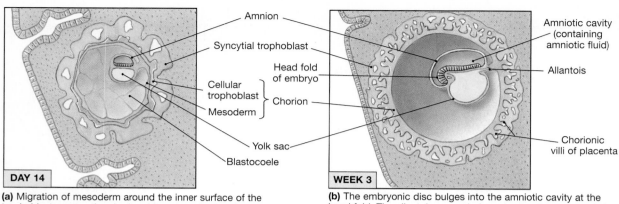

(a) Migration of mesoderm around the inner surface of the trophoblast creates the chorion. Mesodermal migration around the outside of the amniotic cavity, between the ectodermal cells and the trophoblast, creates the amnion. Mesodermal migration around the endodermal pouch creates the yolk sac.

(b) The embryonic disc bulges into the amniotic cavity at the head fold. The allantois, an endodermal extension surrounded by mesoderm, extends toward the trophoblast.

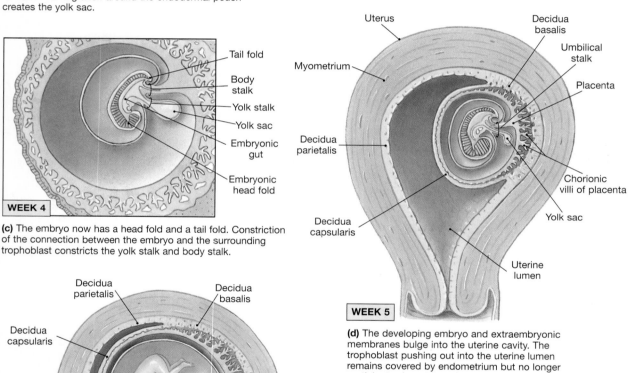

(c) The embryo now has a head fold and a tail fold. Constriction of the connection between the embryo and the surrounding trophoblast constricts the yolk stalk and body stalk.

(d) The developing embryo and extraembryonic membranes bulge into the uterine cavity. The trophoblast pushing out into the uterine lumen remains covered by endometrium but no longer participates in nutrient absorption and embryo support. The embryo moves away from the placenta, and the body stalk and yolk stalk fuse to form an umbilical stalk.

(e) The amnion has expanded greatly, filling the uterine cavity. The fetus is connected to the placenta by an elongated umbilical cord that contains a portion of the allantois, blood vessels, and the remnants of the yolk stalk.

•**FIGURE 29-5 Extraembryonic Membranes and Placenta Formation**

NOTES

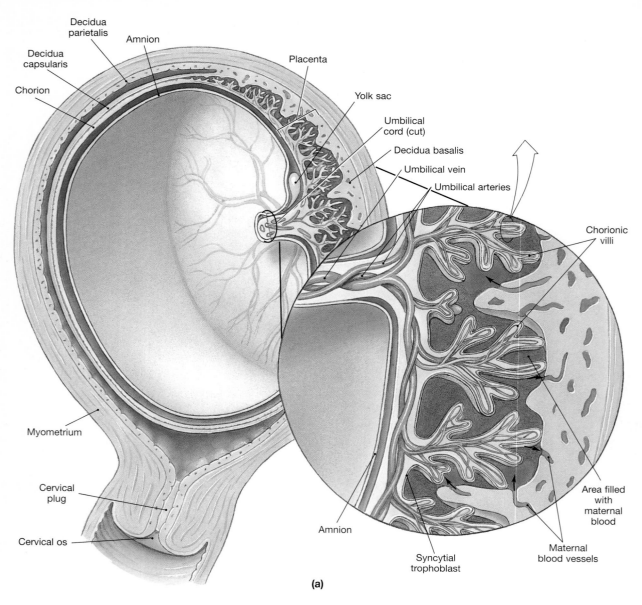

•FIGURE 29-6 A Three-Dimensional View of Placental Structure

NOTES
_____

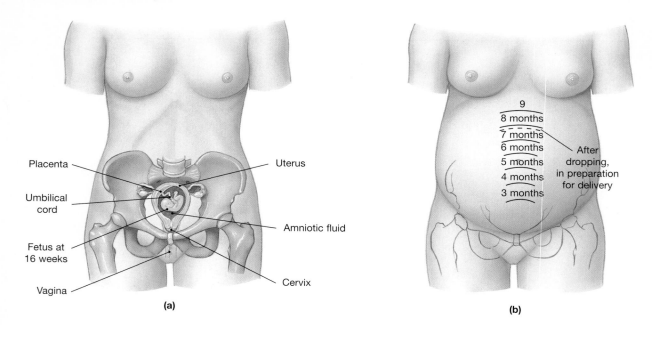

(a)

Placenta

Umbilical cord

Fetus at 16 weeks

Vagina

Uterus

Amniotic fluid

Cervix

(b)

9
8 months
7 months
6 months
5 months
4 months
3 months

After dropping, in preparation for delivery

•FIGURE 29-10 Growth of the Uterus and Fetus

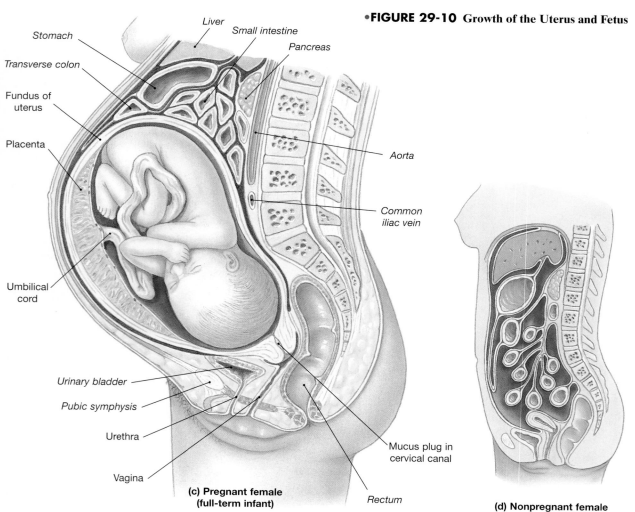

Stomach

Transverse colon

Fundus of uterus

Placenta

Umbilical cord

Urinary bladder

Pubic symphysis

Urethra

Vagina

Liver

Small intestine

Pancreas

Aorta

Common iliac vein

Mucus plug in cervical canal

Rectum

(c) Pregnant female (full-term infant)

(d) Nonpregnant female

NOTES
_____

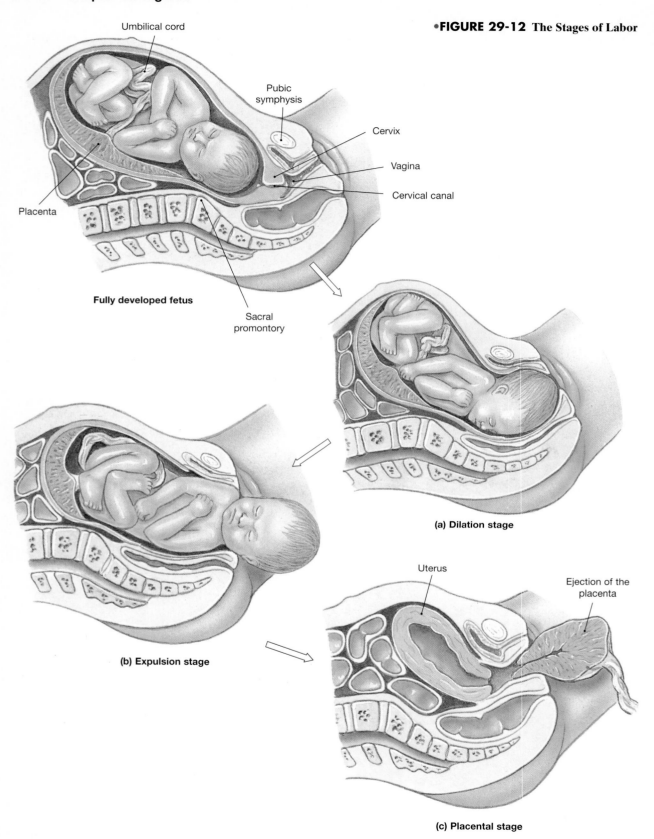

•**FIGURE 29-12** The Stages of Labor

Umbilical cord

Pubic symphysis

Cervix

Vagina

Cervical canal

Placenta

Fully developed fetus

Sacral promontory

(a) Dilation stage

(b) Expulsion stage

Uterus

Ejection of the placenta

(c) Placental stage